Great Gardens to Visit 2011

GW00708335

www.gardenstovisit.net

Are you **looking for new speakers** to come and talk to **your club**?

Each year BBC garden writer and broadcaster, former Head Forester of Westonbirt Arboretum and editor of the annual publication **'Gardens to Visit'**, Tony Russell, undertakes a series of entertaining talks and lectures to garden clubs, horticultural societies and other groups around the country.

All lectures are illustrated with either transparencies or PowerPoint presentation and last for a minimum of one hour plus questions.

For details on Tony's talks and costs please visit
www.gardenstovisit.net or telephone 01453 836730

Great Gardens to Visit 2011

On a recent visit to Japan I was fortunate enough to spend some time in the company of Masayo Miyazaki, President of the Japanese Topiary Society. I was keen to tell her how much I admired Japanese gardens, particularly those situated in and around Kyoto. *"Yes, we have some wonderful gardens in Japan",* was her response, *"and so do you in Great Britain, however what we don't have in Japan is a book like yours which celebrates the very best of British gardens and makes it easy for people to visit them".* It was a special moment for me, to be told by someone from the other side of the world how much they appreciated Gardens to Visit and to know that since our first edition in 2003 the publication has grown into something that is valued both at home and abroad. Of course the creation of the Gardens to Visit website www.gardenstovisit.net in 2008 has helped to broaden the appeal and this now receives literally hundreds of visits every day of the year.

It has been our policy from that very first edition in 2003 to try each year to bring to you a selection of newly discovered gardens, as well as those which have become firm favourites. This year is no exception and I am delighted to be able to report that in this edition we have over forty gardens that were not featured in the 2010 edition of Gardens to Visit. These include Sir Roy Strong's Laskett Gardens in Herefordshire, Mount Pleasant Gardens in Cheshire, Plas Tan y Bwlch in Snowdonia, North Wales and Ham House Gardens near Richmond-upon-Thames in Surrey – all of these proudly take their place alongside long-time favourites such as Batsford Arboretum, Great Dixter, The Lost Gardens of Heligan, The National Botanic Garden of Wales and The Royal Botanic Gardens in Edinburgh.

Throughout 2011 we shall be working closely with The Telegraph, who will be regularly featuring gardens included in this book within their gardening pages which appear every Saturday in the paper. This will be associated with special offers relating to the gardens, so do keep an eye out for these exciting new opportunities.

Finally, it just remains for me to wish you all the very best for 2011 and I hope you have another excellent year of garden visiting.

Tony Russell
November 2010

ngs gardens open for charity

By Visiting an NGS garden you can really make a difference...

Most of the 3,700 gardens that open for the NGS are privately owned and open just a few times each year. A number of gardens open as part of a group, street or village opening which gets the whole community involved.

NGS Gardens welcome group visits

Many gardens that open for the NGS welcome group visits and provide the ideal opportunity for your society or group to visit a garden at a time that is convenient to you.

Gardens which welcome group visits are easily identified in the Yellow Book or on the NGS website - www.ngs.org.uk

Just look out for the telephone symbol. Simply phone the owner and arrange your visit with them at a time which suits you both.

What we do

Every year, NGS gardens across England and Wales welcome over three quarters of a million visitors to them and help the NGS raise much needed funds for the charities that we make donations to. Thanks to the generosity and support of garden, owners, visitors and our volunteer team in 2010 we were able to donate over £2.6m to charity.

The NGS is a registered charity, whose roots can be traced back to 1927. In the last 10 years we have raised over £25 million to help support nursing, caring and garden based charities.

We keep overheads low, so most of the money raised from garden openings goes straight to our beneficiary charities. Donations made by the NGS are 'unrestricted', which means the money can be invested in areas which these charities consider vital to their future development, and which might prove difficult to fund from other sources.

Who we support

In 2010 the NGS made donations to: Macmillan Cancer Support, Marie Curie Cancer Care, Crossroads Care, Help the Hospices, The Queen's Nursing Institute, The Royal Fund for Gardeners' Children, Perennial, National Trust. Arthritis Research UK and the Soldiers Charity - Army Benevolent Fund.

In short, every visitor to an NGS garden is making an essential contribution to someone's life, and especially to those who really need care or support during times of chronic and life-threatening illness.

The National Gardens Scheme - Hatchlands Park, East Clandon, Surrey, GU4 7RT. **www.ngs.org.uk**

Contents

Bedfordshire	7	Hampshire	64-67	Staffordshire	113-114
Berkshire	8-9	Herefordshire	68-72	Surrey	115-119
Buckinghamshire	10-12	Kent	73-82	Sussex - East	120-125
Cambridgeshire	13-17	Leicestershire	83	Sussex - West	126-131
Cheshire	18-24	Lincolnshire	84	Warwickshire	132-133
Cornwall	25-31	London	85	Wiltshire	134-139
Cumbria	32-33	Middlesex	86-88	Worcestershire	140-141
Derbyshire	34-35	Midlands - West	89	Yorkshire	142-153
Devon	36-41	Norfolk	90-94	Channel Islands	154
Dorset	42-46	Northamptonshire	95-99	Scotland	156-165
Essex	47-48	Oxfordshire	100-105	Wales	167-176
Gloucestershire	49-63	Shropshire	106-107	Ireland	177-178
		Somerset	108-112		

England

'A garden is a grand teacher. It teaches patience and careful watchfulness; it teaches industry and thrift; above all it teaches entire trust'.

Gertrude Jekyll

On a recent trip to Japan to view Japanese gardens in and around the Kyoto and Tokyo areas, I was regularly told by my Japanese hosts how much they admired British gardens. As if to make sure I understood this fact, they took me to see the 'English Garden' at Kyu Furukawa, one of the most visited gardens in the whole of Japan. Designed by Josiah Condor, a British architect, it included rose beds, immaculate lawns, clipped box borders and lavender. 'If only we had more gardens like this in Japan,' sighed my host.

I suppose because they are so familiar to us, it is sometimes easy to forget just how special English gardens are and to comprehend just how admired they have become throughout the world. In the pages that follow you will discover some of the finest gardens that England has to offer; perhaps 2011 should be the year when we all re-discover what makes them so special.

Castle Hill Gardens - Devon

The Swiss Garden was created in the early nineteenth century. It contains picturesque features hidden in an undulating nine-acre landscape. The garden is planted with magnificent trees and ornamental shrubs which are arranged in a series of glades, lawns and winding walks, designed to provide unexpected vistas. The recently refurbished and replanted, subterranean grotto and fernery nestles in the centre. 'The Grand Tour' provided inspiration for the tiny thatched Swiss Cottage. The fashion for 'Swiss" architecture, so popular in the Regency period can be seen all around the Garden. Elegant floral arches and a network of ponds with decorative bridges and delightful islands complete the picture. Peafowl roam freely in the garden. Spring bulbs, rhododendrons and rambling roses are spectacular in season. Benches are located at frequent intervals. There is also an adjacent picnic area and a woodland lakeside walk.

Fact File

Opening Times:	November 1st to March 31st 9.30am - 4pm, April 1st to October 31st 9.30am - 5pm
Admission Rates:	Adults £5.00, Senior Citizen £4.00, Accompanied Children Free.
Group Rates:	Minimum group size: 20 but all groups welcome
	Group Rate £4.00, Accompanied Children Free.
Facilities:	Visitor Centre, Restaurant, Toilets, Gift/Souvenirs and Plant Stall.
Disabled Access:	Yes, Toilet and parking for disabled on site. Wheelchairs on loan, booking advised.
Tours/Events:	Guided Tours and Group Bookings by appointment.
Coach Parking:	Yes.
Length of Visit:	2 hours
Booking Contact:	Tony Podmore
	The Swiss Garden, Old Warden Park, Old Warden, Biggleswade, Bedfordshire, SG18 9EP.
	Telephone: 01767 627923 Fax: 01767 627949
Email:	tony.podmore@shuttleworth.org
Website:	www.shuttleworth.org
Location:	Approximately 2 miles west of Biggleswade A1 roundabout signposted from A1 and A600.

Please quote this guide when making a booking

Savill Garden - Windsor Great Park Berkshire

World-renowned 35 acres of ornamental gardens and woodland, including National Collections and rare international species, The Savill Garden provides a wealth of beauty and interest in all seasons.

Do not miss the exciting new Rose Garden. The contemporary design will create an intense sensory experience with roses especially chosen for their scent, strong colours and repeat flowering.

Spring in the Savill Garden is heralded by hosts of daffodils, marvellous magnolias and the wonderful perfume of the varieties of rhododendrons and azaleas. Summer brings a contrast of colour, with the vibrancy of the grand Herbaceous Borders and the tranquil, pastel shades of the Golden Jubilee Garden. The glorious displays of autumn in the Garden are a joy to behold, before attention turns to the striking new additions to the Winter Garden. The Queen Elizabeth Temperate House showcases original and unusual seasonal plant displays which offer continuous floral interest and vitality throughout the year.

Plus, the award-winning Savill Building offers excellent shopping, an art gallery, exhibitions and a restaurant, managed by Leith's.

Fact File

Opening Times: 10am - 6pm March - October, 10am - 4.30pm November - February (last admission to the Garden is 30 minutes before closing).

Admission Rates: Adults: £8.50, Senior Citizens: £7.95, Child (6-16): £3.75, Family: £21.00.

Group Rates: £6.95 per person for groups of 10 or more.

Seasonal Prices: Prices shown are peak prices, (March 11 - October 11). Please contact The Savill Garden for off peak prices.

Facilities: Shop, Plant Sales, Teas, Restaurant.

Disabled Access: Yes. Toilet and Parking for disabled on site. Wheelchairs available to loan.

Tours/Events: Guided tours are available, (please book your tour two week prior to visit)
Ongoing programme of events and exhibitions. Please visit www.theroyallandscape.co.uk or contact The Savill Garden for details.

Coach Parking: Yes.

Length of Visit: 3 - 4 hours

Booking Contact: Carla Hall
Crown Estate Office, The Great Park, Windsor, Berkshire, SL4 2HT
Telephone: 0845 603 6228 Fax: 01753 624107

Email: enquiries@theroyallandscape.co.uk

Website: www.theroyallandscape.co.uk

Please quote this guide when making a booking

Valley Gardens - Windsor Great Park Surrey

A woodland garden on the grand scale; set beneath the canopies of beautiful mature trees with delightful views to Virginia Water Lake. Over 200 acres of camellias rhododendrons, magnolias and many other flowering trees and shrubs provide visitors with breathtaking displays in March, April and May.

Massed plantings of hydrangeas are the highlight of the summer before a myriad of autumn tints from Japanese maples, birches, sweet gums and tupelos light up the woods.

Winter brings the flowers of witch-hazel and drifts of heathers amongst the dwarf conifers in the Heather Garden before swathes of dwarf daffodils stud the turf in the sweeping Azalea Valley.

Truly a garden for all seasons.

Fact File

Opening times:	Car park open: 8am - 7pm (4pm in winter) or sunset if earlier.
Admission Rates:	Car Park Charges: £6.00
Facilities:	At nearby Savill Garden.
Disabled Access:	Limited. Toilet and parking for disabled on site. Wheelchair trail in the garden. Wheelchair accessible viewing platform for the Punch Bowl display.
Tours/Events:	None.
Coach Parking:	Coaches by arrangement on weekdays only (Charge applies).
Length of Visit:	2 - 3 hours
Booking Contact:	Carla Hall Crown Estate Office, The Great Park, Windsor, Berkshire, SL4 2HT Telephone: 0845 603 6228 Fax: 01753 624107
Email:	enquiries@theroyallandscape.co.uk
Website:	www.theroyallandscape.co.uk
Location:	On the eastern boundary of Windsor Great Park (off A30) Access to Valley Gardens car park via Wick Road.

Chenies Manor House   Buckinghamshire

Winner of the Historic House & Christie's Garden of the Year 2009 Award.

Home of the MacLeod Matthews family, this 14th & 15th century Manor House with fortified tower is the original home of the Earls of Bedford, visited by Henry VIII and Elizabeth I.

The Manor is surrounded by five acres of enchanting gardens, famed for the spring display of 6,000 tulips and then from early June there is a succession of colour throughout the gardens. The Physic Garden contains a wide selection of medical & culinary herbs. The Parterre has an ancient Oak and a complicated Yew Maze, while the kitchen garden is in Victorian style with unusual vegetables & fruit.

Chenies Manor Plant & Garden Fair.
The famous Plant Fair with 70 specialist nurseries is on Sunday 17th July 2011, 10-5pm. Adults £6 (this includes entry to the Manor Gardens). The house opens at 2pm extra £4.

Fact File

Opening Times:	April to October Inclusive. Every Wednesday and Thursday and all Bank Holiday Mondays 2-5pm.
Admission:	Adults Garden Only £5
	Adults House & Garden £6.50
	Children Garden £3
	Children House & Garden £4
Facilities:	Home made Teas, Lunches for groups (by arrangement only)
Disabled Access:	To the Gardens and Tea Room only (disabled lavatory provided).
Car & Coach:	Ample car and coach parking
Length of visit:	2-3 hours.
Booking contact:	Susan Brock
Telephone:	01494 762888
Email:	macleodmatthews@btinternet.com
Website:	cheniesmanorhouse.co.uk
Location:	Ref: TQ016 984
Directions:	M25 – Jct 18 – A404 towards Amersham.

Please quote this guide when making a booking

A country retreat on a grand scale, Cliveden's magnificent gardens and breath-taking views have been admired for centuries.

Cliveden was the glittering hub of society; visited by virtually every British Monarch since George I and home to Waldorf and Nancy Astor in the early 20th century. Cliveden hosted exclusive parties and political gatherings and in the 1960s become infamously associated with the Profumo Affair.

Today, you can relax in grand style as you explore the stunning gardens which feature the celebrated Parterre, season long floral displays, distinctive topiary and an outstanding sculpture collection. The Parterre has been beautifully restored with colourful bedding based on the original designs by John Fleming and the spring display of 10,000 hyacinths in the Long Garden will be a treat for the senses. Complete your day out with delicious home-cooked lunches and teas at the Orangery café and a visit to the National Trust gift shop.

Fact File

Opening times:	19 Feb - 30 Oct - daily, 10 a.m. - 5.30 p.m. 31 Oct - 23 Dec - daily, 10 a.m. - 4.00 p.m.
Admission Rates:	Gift Aid admission* Adults: £9.00, Child: £4.50, Family: £22.50. NT members free.
	* Including a voluntary 10% donation; visitors can, however, choose to pay the standard admission prices which are displayed at the property and at www.nationaltrust.org.uk
Group Rates:	Minimum Group Size: 15 Adults: £7.65 – Not Sundays
Facilities:	Visitor Centre, Shop, Plant Sales, Restaurant, Teas, Film.
Disabled Access:	Yes. Wheelchair loan available
Toilets on site:	Yes
Car Parking on site:	Yes
Coach Parking:	Yes
Guided Tours:	Yes, booking required.
Length of Visit:	2 - 3 hours
Booking Contact:	Gill Coop, Cliveden, Taplow, Nr. Maidenhead, Buckinghamshire, SL6 0JA Booking Tel No.01628 605069. Booking Fax No. 01628 669461
Email:	cliveden@nationaltrust.org.uk
Website:	www.nationatrust.org.uk/cliveden
Location:	M4 Junction 7 to A4 or M40 Junction 4 to A404 and follow brown signs. Coach entrance on Bourne End Road

Please quote this guide when making a booking

Waddesdon Manor and Gardens were bequeathed to the National Trust by the Rothschilds in 1957. The garden today is essentially the one laid out by Baron Ferdinand de Rothschild and his French, landscape designer, Elie Lainé.

It is considered one of the finest Victorian gardens in Britain with a parterre, seasonal displays, colourful shrubs, carpet bedding, statuary, fountains and parkland. At its heart lies the rococo-style Aviary housing exotic birds and known for breeding endangered species. The Aviary glade is the location of a new acquisition called Perceval by Sarah Lucas, a life-sized, bronze horse and cart. Sarah is of the same generation of artists as Damien Hirst and the late Angus Fairhust, whose gorilla sculpture can be seen in an area called the Tulip Patch.

The garden can be enjoyed at any season. Guided walks take place from April to September.

Fact File

Opening times:	Gardens, Aviary, Woodland Playground, Shops and Restaurant - 10.00-5.00pm
Admission Rates:	Winter Season: 8th Jan-27th Mar (weekends only), Adult: £8.00, Child: £4.50, Family: £20.50
	Rest of the Year: 30th Mar-31st Dec (Weds-Fri), Adult: £6.50, Child: £3.50, Family: £16.50
	30th Mar-31st Dec (weekends & BHs), Adult: £8.00, Child: £4.50, Family: £20.50,
	(Including Tuesday 26th April. Monday 19th & Tuesdays 20th & 27th December)
	Closed 24th, 25th, 26th December. NT members free.
Group Rates:	Minimum Group Size: 15.
	Group rates available see www.waddesdon.org.uk or phone the booking contact (see below).
Facilities:	Shops, Plant Centre, Restaurant, Woodland Playground
Disabled Access:	Yes. Wheelchair loan available.
Toilets on site:	Yes
Car Parking on site:	Yes
Coach Parking:	Yes
Guided Walks:	Yes
Length of Visit:	1 – 4 hours
Special Events:	Yes
Booking Contact:	Deborah Read, Waddesdon Manor, Waddesdon, Nr. Aylesbury, Buckinghamshire HP18 0JH
	Booking Tel No.01296 653226. Booking Fax No. 01296 653212
Email:	deborah.read@nationaltrust.org.uk
Website:	www.waddesdon.org.uk
Location:	20 minutes from Junction 7 (northbound) and 9 (southbound) off the M40, off the A41 between Aylesbury and Bicester.

Please quote this guide when making a booking

Anglesey Abbey, Gardens & Lode Mill Cambridgeshire

A passion for tradition and style inspired one man to transform a run-down country house. The glorious Jacobean-style country house is now set amidst a magnificent landscape. At the age of 30, the 1st Lord Fairhaven sought to inspire and surprise. He created a spectacular garden, encompassing 114 acres of rolling lawns, sweeping avenues, formal gardens, classical statuary, wildflower meadows, wildlife discovery area and a working watermill.

Throughout the year, changing colours and scents provide a unique experience. Rare varieties of snowdrops create a popular display in January and February; thousands of hyacinths highlight spring, while summer is celebrated by colourful herbaceous borders and dahlias. Magnificent autumn foliage is followed by glorious winter colours, making Anglesey a garden for all seasons.

Over 100 pieces of classical garden statuary nestle against the backdrop of Anglesey's stunning Emperors' Walk, Arboretum, Herbaceous Border and Coronation and Cross Avenues. A true showcase for twentieth century English garden design.

Photo - Brian & Nina Chapple

Fact File

Opening times: Gardens/restaurant/shop/plant centre 1 January - 27 February 10.30- 4.30 Monday to Sunday 28 Feb - 30 October 10.30 - 5.30 Monday to Sunday. 31 October - 31 December 10.30 - 4.30 Monday to Sunday.
House - 2 March - 30 October 11.00 - 5.00 Wednesday - Sunday. Open BH Mons and Good Friday. Closed Christmas Eve, Christmas Day and Boxing Day. Garden areas open according to Season. Snowdrop Season 24 Jan - 27 Feb 2011.

Admission Rates: Garden only: Adult £6.25, Child £3.10, Family £15.60, Family (1 Adult) £9.35
* Includes a voluntary 10% gift aid donation towards the upkeep and restoration of the property. Standard rates available on request.

Group Rates: Minimum Group Size: 15. Garden only: Adult £5.30, Child £2.60

Facilities: Visitor Centre, restaurant, shop, plant sales, second-hand bookshop

Disabled Access: Disabled toilets. Parking. Wheelchairs & PMVs available booking essential. Mill: access to lower floor only, ramp available.

Parking: Onsite. Coach parking booking essential

Length of Visit: Minimum 2 hours

Guided Tours: Yes, booking essential.

Special Events: Special events programme, for details see website or Tel. 01223 810080

Booking Contact: Administrator, Anglesey Abbey, Gardens & Lode Mill, Quy Rd, Lode, Cambridge CB25 9EJ. Tel No. 01223 810080. Fax No. 01223 810088

Email: angleseyabbey@nationaltrust.org.uk

Website: www.nationaltrust.org.uk/angleseyabbey

Location: 6 miles north-east of Cambridge on B1102. Signed from A14, junc 35.

Please quote this guide when making a booking

Cambridge University Botanic Garden   Cambridge

The heritage-listed Cambridge University Botanic Garden was the vision of John Henslow, mentor to Charles Darwin. Today the Garden is a showcase for over 8000 plant species from around the world, including nine national collections, all immaculately displayed amongst the finest arboretum in the region.

Highlights include the Winter Garden, the original masterclass in combining foliage, flower and fragrance for winter interest; the Rock Garden, with its kaleidoscopic flowering and vantage point over the Lake, teeming with birdlife; the Dry Garden, a beautiful, water-wise planting; the buzzing Bee Borders and the Scented Garden, full of herbs and roses, are summer highpoints. Diverse global habitats, from arid lands of architectural cactus to flamboyant, tropical rainforests, can be explored in the warmth of the magnificently-restored Glasshouse.

The Garden offers year-round inspiration for gardeners, is an exciting introduction to the natural world for families, and a great day out for everyone.

Fact File

Opening Times: Both the award-winning Brookside Gate & Station Road Gate are open every day from 10am. January, November & December 10am-4pm, February, March & October 10am-5pm, April - September 10am-6pm. The Garden is closed from 24 December - 1 January inclusive.

Admission Rates: Adult: £4.00, Concession: £3.50 (Over 60's & students with an identification card) Children (0-16) Free (Children must be accompanied by an adult at all times) Friends of CUBG Free, Cambridge University students, Free (with a valid University Card)

Group Rates: Minimum group size: 10. Prices As above.

Facilities: Botanic Garden Shop with Plant Sales. Café for light meals, teas, refreshments.

Disabled Access: Yes and toilets on site.

Tours Events: Yes - booking is required.

Car/Coach Parking: No

Length of Visit: At least a half day is recommended.

Booking Contact: Di Harrison or Pat Smith 1, Brookside, Cambridge, CB2 1JE. Tel: 01223 336265

Email: enquiries@botanic.cam.ac.uk

Website: www.botanic.cam.ac.uk

Location: If travelling by car, please use the Trumpington Road Park & Ride (off J11, M11, open daily). If coming by coach, there is coach drop-off only at the corner of Trumpington Road and Bateman Street. Coaches must then go to one of Cambridge's designated coach parks and return to pick up.

Elgood's Brewery Gardens   Cambridgeshire

A beautiful 4-acre garden, situated behind Elgood's Brewery, on the banks of the River Nene in Wisbech, in the heart of the Fens.

The garden is famous for its maze and its trees, some over 200 years old, including Ginkgo Biloba, Tulip Tree, and Tree of Heaven. There is a lake with golden and ghost carp, a pond, which is home to Great Crested Newts, and a hot-house with many exotic plants.

The Visitor Centre houses a museum with brewery artefacts and pub memorabilia. A variety of freshly prepared snacks are available in the licensed cafe-bar and there is a well-stocked shop selling quality beers, gifts and plants.

Close by are The Octavia Hill Museum, The Wisbech & Fenland Museum, and the National Trust's Peckover House. These attractions, together with several excellent pubs along the riverbanks, add up to an enjoyable and interesting visit.

Fact File

Opening Times: 26th April - 29th September 2011 11.30am - 4.30pm. Sunday 5th June & Sunday 3rd July Garden open 1pm - 4.30pm, Sunday 7th August in aid of National Garden scheme 1pm - 4.30pm, Garden only - limited catering (no lunches)

Admission Rates: Garden & Brewery - Adults £6.50, Senior Citizens £6.50, Child (6-16) £4.00
We regret that children under 6 are not permitted on Brewery Tours
Garden only - Adults £3.00, Senior Citizen £2.50, Child £2.50

Groups Rates: Minimum group size 10
Garden & Brewery - £5.50, Garden Only - £2.50

Facilities: Visitor Centre, Gift Shop, Plant Sales, Teas, Licensed bar, Free Parking.
No dogs except guide dogs.

Disabled Access: Yes. Toilets and parking for disabled on site. Wheelchairs on loan. Booking Advisable.

Tours/Events: Brewery Tours Tues, Wed, and Thurs 2pm (not suitable for disabled) Garden show and Craft Fair 8th May & 4th September 10am - 4pm.
Christmas open weekend (free entry - free tours) 3rd/4th December.

Coach Parking: Yes

Length of Visit: 1 - 2+ Hours

Booking Contact: Kate Pateman, North Brink, Wisbech, Cambridge, PE13 1LN
Telephone: 01945 583160   Fax: 01945 587711

Email: info@elgoods-brewery.co.uk

Website: www.elgoods-brewery.co.uk

Location: Wisbech

Please quote this guide when making a booking

Elton Hall Gardens Cambridgeshire

Elton Hall Gardens have been stunningly restored during the last twenty years. The present layout is based on the Edwardian design which included the earlier medieval and Victorian gardens. Immaculately kept hedges of hornbeam and yew encompass four different areas.

The main lawn has a mass of topiary and an enchanting sunken lily pond which is surrounded with beds containing a number of specimen plants.

The former rose garden has recently been redesigned and is now a magical flower garden with a modern fountain and wisteria clad arches.

The Millennium was celebrated by the building of an orangery and this is set in a colourful Mediterranean garden with lemon and orange trees.

A small shrubbery area, with such gems as Paulownia Tomentosa, leads the visitor back into the Box Walk to enjoy another view of the house set in these magnificent gardens.

Fact File

Opening Times:	2.00 p.m. – 5.00 p.m.: May Bank Holiday Sunday 29th May and Monday 30th May; Wednesday & Thursdays in June & July, Wednesday, Thursday and Sundays in August; August Bank Holiday, Monday 29th August.
Admission Rates:	Adults: £5.50, Senior Citizens: £5.00, Children: Accompanied children under 16 admitted free
Group Rates:	Minimum Group Size: 20. Adults: £5.50
Facilities:	Shop, plant sales, restaurant, teas, toilets.
Disabled Access:	Yes – to garden
Car Parking on site:	Yes
Coach Parking:	Yes
Tours/Events:	Free flow or guided tours available. Booking required.
Length of Visit:	1 hour
Booking Contact:	The Administrator Elton Hall Gardens, Elton Hall Nr. Peterborough, Cambridgeshire PE8 6SH Booking Telephone No. 01832 280468 Booking Fax No. 01832 280584
Email:	office@eltonhall.com
Website:	www.eltonhall.com
Location:	Elton is located just off the A605 between Peterborough and Oundle.

Please quote this guide when making a booking

Peckover House is an elegant Georgian merchant's house within the heart of Wisbech, built in 1722. For one hundred and fifty years it was lived in by the Peckover family, a Quaker banking dynasty. The outstanding two-acre garden is a rare gem of surprising size, hidden behind the backs of neighbouring properties. It is regarded as one of the finest walled town gardens in the country, and its "gardenesque" character offers a rambling perambulation through distinct areas, with vistas through gaps and internal walls. The garden contains notable trees, such as Ginko Biloba (Maidenhair tree), Liriodendron tulipiferum (Tulip Tree), and possibly the largest specimen of Cornus mas in the country. The garden also contains three summerhouses, two pool gardens, over 70 species of rose and a croquet lawn. The Victorian glasshouses include an Orangery with 300-year-old orange trees which still fruit prolifically.

Fact File

Opening times: 19th February - 6th March 2011, Saturday, Sunday only 12 - 4pm.
12th March - 30th October 2011, Saturday, Sunday, Monday, Tuesday, Wednesday 12 - 5pm
Also open all week 9th - 27th April, 30th May - 3rd June, 27th June - 1st July, 24th-28th October.

Admission Rates: Adults: £6.60, Children: £3.30, Family: £16.50
National Trust members: Free

Group Rates: Minimum Group Size: 15. Adults: £5.60 Booking necessary

Facilities: Shop, Plant Sales, Tea Room, Secondhand bookshop

Disabled Access: Yes, level access. PMV loan (book in advance)
Toilet on site. No parking on site – drop-off point available.

Tours/Events: House and garden tours, day and evening tours available.

Coach Parking: No, available nearby

Length of Visit: 2+ hours.

Booking Contact: Property Secretary
Peckover House and Garden, North Brink, Wisbech, Cambridgeshire PE13 1JR
Tel: 01945 583463

Email: peckover@nationaltrust.org.uk

Website: www.nationaltrust.org.uk/peckover

Location: Centre of Wisbech, on north bank of River Nene.

Please quote this guide when making a booking

Cheshire's gardens
Different every day

There are over **25 beautiful Gardens of Distinction** in Cheshire and each promises a unique adventure.

From stately homes and secret gardens, the quintessentially English to exotic oriental planting – Cheshire is Home to England's Finest Gardens.

Discover more at visitcheshire.com/gardens

Cheshire's Gardens
of Distinction

Home of England's Finest Gardens

Arley Hall & Gardens

The award winning gardens, recently voted in the top 50 in Europe and in Britain's top 10, have been lovingly created over 250 years with each generation of the family making its own contribution. The result is a garden of great atmosphere, interest and vitality, which blends strong elements of design from earlier centuries with modern ideas in both planting and design. Arley is, therefore, a wonderful example of the idea that the best gardens are living, changing works of art. Outstanding features are the renowned double herbaceous border (c1846) the Quercus Ilex and pleached Lime Avenues, Victorian rootree, walled gardens, yew hedges and shrub rose collection. The family tradition continues today with the current Viscount Ashbrook, who over the last 30 years has created the less formal Grove and Woodland Walk, where 300 varieties of rhododendron grow amongst a collection of rare trees and shrubs in a delightful tranquil setting.

Fact File

Opening Times: April 2nd 2011 to October 30th 2011 plus weekends in November.

Admission Rates: Gardens: Adults: £7.00, Seniors: £6.50, Children 5-16: £2.50, Family 2+2: £16.50, Hall & Gardens: Adults: £10.00, Seniors: £9.00, Children 5-12: £4.00.

Group Rates: Gardens: £6.50, Seniors: £6.00, Children: £2.00
Hall & Gardens: Adults: £9.00, Seniors: £8.00, Children 5-12: £3.50, Family 2+2: £25.00
Season tickets: Adult single: £35.00, Adult Joint: £60.00, Children 5-16: £15.00, Family 2+2: £85.
Tour of Gardens with Head Gardener - £80.00 (max 25 visitors)
Tour of Hall - £40.00 (max 25 visitors)

Facilities: Shop, Plant Nursery, Licensed Restaurant, Teas, Picnic & Play Area, Chapel, Estate Walks.

Disabled Access: Yes. Toilet and parking on site. Wheelchair available booking (recommended for special events).

Tours/Events: Please check website for details.

Coach Parking: Yes.

Length of Visit: 2 hours

Booking Contact: Sue Ellams, Estate Secretary, Arley Hall & Gardens, Northwich, Cheshire CW9 6NA
Telephone: 01565 777353 Fax: 01565 777465

Email: enquiries@arleyhallandgardens.com

Website: www.arleyhallandgardens.com

Location: M6 – Junction 19 or 20, M56 Junction 9 or 10. Brown tourist signs from Northwich and Knutsford, both 6 miles approximately.

Please quote this guide when making a booking

Cholmondeley Castle Garden is said by many to be among the most romantically beautiful gardens they have seen. Even the wild orchids, daisies and buttercups take on an aura of glamour in this beautifully landscaped setting. Visitors enter by the deer park mere – one of two strips of water which are home to many types of waterfowl and freshwater fish. Those who take advantage of the picnic site can walk round the lake and enjoy the splendid view of Cholmondeley Castle which stands so dramatically on the hill surrounded by sweeping lawns and magnificent trees: two enormous cedars of Lebanon and great spreading oaks among sweet chestnut, lime, beech and plane. Whatever the season there is always a wealth of plants and shrubs in flower from the earliest bulbs through many varieties of magnolia, camellia, azalea and rhododendrons. Followed by golden canopied laburnum grove, a very fine davidia involucrate in the glade, and varieties of cornus.

There is also a very pretty rose garden surrounded by mixed borders, containing a large variety of herbaceous plants and shrubs.

Fact File

Opening Times:	3rd April 2011 to 29th September 2011 Wednesday, Thursday, Sundays and Bank Holidays 11am - 5pm. Autumn tints 16th, 23rd and 30th October 2011. Castle only open on limited days, for groups only, by pre-arrangement.
Admission Rates:	Adults: £5.00, Children: £2.00 from ages 5 to 16.
Group Rates:	Minimum Group Size: 25
Facilities:	Gift Shop, Teas and Garden Nursery Plant Sales.
Disabled Access:	Yes. Toilet and parking for disabled on site.
Tours/Events:	Please ring to enquire about special events, plays, concerts
Car Parking:	Yes.
Coach Parking:	Yes.
Length of Visit:	6 hours
Booking Contact:	Cholmondeley Castle, Malpas, Cheshire SY14 8AH Tel. 01829 720383 Fax. 01829 720877
Email:	dilys@cholmondeleycastle.co.uk
Website:	www.cholmondeleycastle.com
Location:	7 miles west of Nantwich, 6 miles north of Whitchurch on A49. Sat Nav SY14 8ET

Please quote this guide when making a booking

Mount Pleasant Gardens has been created from a blank canvas in just 14 years and now extends to over 10 acres. Never intended to be opened to the public, the garden visitor now has the rare opportunity to explore a new vibrant garden that has been solely created and gardened by its owners Dave and Louise (Darlington), purely to indulge their passion for plants and nature. The garden has a tropical feel because of its many cordylines and palms and bold planting schemes, which are packed full of so many plants.

Due to its location on an open and sometimes windy hillside, shelter-belts firstly had to be established, but the south-westerly aspect and numerous springs, enabled the garden to rapidly develop into a lush and deceptively mature landscape that cascades down the hillside, with magnificent views across to the Welsh Hills.

Fact File

Opening Times:	2nd April – Sept 28th. April – August, Wednesdays, Saturdays, Sundays 12 – 5pm, September, Wednesday, Thursday, Friday, Saturday, Sunday 12- 5pm.
Admission Rates:	Adults and Senior Citizens £4.00, Children £1.00 during normal opening hours.
Group Rates:	Minimum group size 20 £5.00.
Facilities:	Plant Sales, Teas and Sculptures for sale.
Disabled Access:	Ring prior to visit.
Toilets on Site:	Yes.
Car Parking:	Yes.
Coach Parking:	Yes.
Wheelchair Loan:	No.
Length of Visit:	1 - 2 hours.
Special Events:	September Sculpture Exhibition.
Booking Contact:	Louise Darlington, Mount Pleasant Gardens, Yeld Lane, Kelsall, Cheshire, CW6 0TB. Telephone: 01829 751592
Email:	louisedarlington@btinternet.com
Website:	www.mountpleasantgardens.co.uk
Location:	8 miles east of Chester, turn off the A54 at the traffic lights into Chester Road, Kelsall, turn right into Yeld Lane.

Please quote this guide when making a booking

Ness Botanic Gardens celebrate a unique double - winning a Gold Medal and The Best in Show Award for the second year running, at The RHS Tatton Show in July 2009.

The highly imaginative show garden created by Chris Beardshaw, award winning designer and TV presenter has created this unique garden for Ness entitled 'Ness Botanische, Cheshire's Gardens of Distinction – Under the Microscope'.

The superb gardens at Ness on the Wirral Peninsular, overlooking the Dee Estuary were founded in 1898 by Arthur Kilpin Bulley, a Liverpool cotton merchant with a passion for gardens and for plant hunting.

Our Visitor Centre provides a warm welcome to the Gardens incorporating the multi award winning Roses Tea Rooms, gift shop and plant sales. An extensive events programme runs throughout the year including guided walks, Sunday lectures, courses, children's half term activities, see our website for details www.nessgardens.org.uk Much of the garden is accessible for those of limited mobility and both courtesy wheelchairs and motorised buggies are available FREE, advance booking recommended.

Fact File

Opening Times:	1st Feb – 31st Oct: 10 a.m. - 5 p.m. 1st Nov - 31st Jan: 10 a.m. - 4.30 p.m.
Admission Charges:	Admission to Gardens apply.
On-Site Facilities:	Visitor Centre, Shop, Plant Sales, Licensed Café, Teas, Lecture Theatre
Disabled Access:	Yes, partial. Wheelchair and mobility scooter loan available, booking required.
Toilets on site:	Yes
Car Parking on site:	Yes
Coach Parking:	Yes
Guided Tours:	Yes, booking required
Length of Visit:	Approx. 2½ hours
Special Events:	See www.nessgardens.org.uk
Booking Contact:	Visitor Services, Ness Botanic Gardens, Ness, Neston, South Wirral, Cheshire CH64 4AY. Booking Tel No. 0151 353 0123 Booking Fax No. 0151 353 1004
Email:	nessgdns@liv.ac.uk
Website:	www.nessgardens.org.uk
Location:	Road: off A540 Chester-Hoylake Road.

Please quote this guide when making a booking

Rode Hall Gardens were created by three notable landscape designers; Humphry Repton drew up the plans for the landscape and Rode Pool in his 'Red Book' of 1790. Between 1800 and 1810 John Webb, a Cheshire landscapist, constructed the Pool, an artificial lake of approximately 40 acres and at the same time he created the terraced rock garden and grotto. This area is covered in snowdrops in February followed by daffodils and bluebells and colour continues with the flowering of many specie and hybrid rhododendrons and azaleas in May.

In 1860 William Nesfield designed the rose garden and terrace where the flowerbeds are now filled with roses and a variety of herbaceous plants.

The two-acre walled kitchen garden dates from 1750 and grows a wide variety of flowers, vegetables and fruit. An Italian garden is being developed in the ruins of the old `Tenants Hall.

There is a fine icehouse and the Hall is open to the public on Wednesdays.

Fact File

Opening times: Snowdrop walks: From 29th January to 13th March – daily except Mondays. 12–4pm. 1 April to 30 September: Tuesdays, Wednesdays, Thursdays and Bank Holidays (not Good Friday): 12 noon - 5pm.

Admission Rates: Adults: £4.00, Senior Citizens £3.00, Children under 16 free.

Group Rates: Minimum Groups Size: 10

Facilities: Shop, plant sales, teas, light lunches.

Disabled Access: Limited. Toilet and car parking on site

Tours/Events: Guided tours available.

Coach Parking: Yes

Length of Visit: 1 hour.

Booking Contact: Sharon Brown. Rode Hall Gardens, Rode Hall, Scholar Green, Cheshire ST7 3QN Telephone: 01270 882961 - 873237 Fax: 01270 882962

Email: enquiries@rodehall.co.uk

Website: www.rodehall.co.uk

Location: 5 miles south of Congleton, between A34 and A50.

Please quote this guide when making a booking

The gardens were created from a wetland area around a tranquil pool in a sheltered valley on the edge of Delamere Forest.

This is an informal garden where shade and moisture loving plants, including Primulas, Astilbes and Hostas grow amongst natural wooded areas. Paths lead the visitor over bridges, to an unusual island where groups of Alder and Willow grow through the water, reminiscent of "the everglades". At the poolside, trees include the Swamp Cypress and the Dawn Redwood.

The beautiful views across the pool to the cottage gardens lead the eye over waterside Iris, giant marsh Marigolds and borders of summer flowering perennials, set around some rarer trees and shrubs.

Many of the plants featured in the gardens are grown on site at our nursery, which has a good range of interesting perennials and exotic plants. Our tearoom serves light refreshments and cream teas for groups.

Fact File

Opening Times: 10.00am - 5.00pm Tuesday – Sunday and Bank Holiday Mondays. 2nd April – 30th October. (Group visits also welcome any day or evening and Mondays by appointment)

Admission Rates: Adults £3.00, Senior Citizens £3.00, Children free.

Group Rates: Minimum Group size 10, includes guided tour lasting about 45 minutes.

Group tour: Adults and Senior Citizens £3.50, Children free. Group tour incl. cream teas: £6.00.

Facilities: Tearoom serving light refreshments.

Disabled Access: Most areas accessible some steps and gravel paths.

Toilets on site: Yes

Car Parking: Yes

Length of Visit: 30 minutes to 1 hour depending on level of plant interest.

Special Events: Plant Hunters Fair, Bank Holiday Monday 30th May 10am-3pm.

Booking Contact: Tony Overland, Stonyford Cottage, Oakmere, Northwich, Cheshire, CW8 2TF. Booking Tel No. 01606 888970/888128 (answerphone)

Email: stonyfordcottage@yahoo.co.uk

Website: www.stonyfordcottagegardens.co.uk

Location: From Northwich take the A556 towards Chester, 3/4 mile past A556/A49 junction, follow the brown signs on A556.

Please quote this guide when making a booking

Burncoose Nurseries   Cornwall

This 30-acre woodland gardens and nursery boasts award-winning displays and flowering features to captivate garden-enthusiasts and horticultural amateurs alike.

Perched on a hilltop, is home to one of the most diverse ranges of plants in the region. Its sprawling woodland gardens and old flower garden are rich with the likes of camellias, azaleas and rhododendrons, as well as over 20 species of bamboo.

Its vast acreage is packed with prolific blooms all year round and you can take self-guided wanders to appreciate the beauty of the successive seasons.

On a Spring ramble witness the drifts of snowdrops, primroses and wild violets, and later the daffodils and blankets of nodding bluebells. On a Summer wander it is the hydrangeas that spread their purple-blues and swamp the fading blooms of Spring. Take an Autumn amble, when more subtle colours and hardy specimens still leave much to be discovered

Fact File

Opening Times:	Monday – Saturday: 8.30 – 5 p.m. Sunday 11 a.m. – 5 p.m.
Admission Charges:	(to gardens only, nursery free): Adults: £3.00. Conducted tour £5.00 each
On-Site Facilities:	Shop, Plant Sales, Teas
Disabled Access:	Yes
Toilets on site:	Yes
Car Parking on site:	Yes
Coach Parking:	Yes
Length of Visit:	1½ - 2 hours
Booking Contact:	Stephen Dance, Burncoose Nurseries, Gwennap, Redruth, Cornwall TR16 6BJ
	Telephone No. 01209 860316 Fax No. 01209 860011
Email:	info@burncoose.co.uk
Website:	www.burncoose.co.uk
Location:	On A393 betweenRedruth and Falmouth approximately half-way
	between villages of Lanner and Ponsanooth.

This informal woodland garden created in the late 19th and early 20th century by J C Williams, is today the home of many fine examples of plants brought back by the intrepid plant hunters of the early 20th century and also a wide range of rhododendrons, camellias and magnolias, both bred and raised here, which the Williams family and Caerhays Gardens have become famous for worldwide.

Caerhays Castle is of the very few Nash built castles still standing and is situated within the 60 acre garden. Caerhays Garden is home to the famous williamsii camellias and also home to a National Magnolia Collection and was found, by a representative of the Tree Register, recently to contain no less than 78 Champion Trees (thought to be the most in a private garden in England).

Fact File

Opening Times:	Gardens 14th February 2011 to 5th June 2011 10am to 5 pm Last entry 4.30
	Seven days a week. House 14th March 14th to 3rd June 12.00 -3.00
	Weekdays only (reservations recommended).
Admission Rates:	Garden or House, £7.50 (adults), £6.50 (OAP) £3.50 (Under 16)
	Combined Ticket, £9.50 (adults), £4.50 (Under 16)
Group Rates:	Special group rates (Min 15 pers) or Private guided tours of the garden only by appointment
Facilities:	Shop, plant sales area, licensed tea rooms serving lunches and snacks
Disabled Access:	Partial, steep paths to top of garden but drive and lower routes fully accessible.
	Disabled toilet in courtyard. Disabled parking by entry.
Tours\Events:	Contact Estate Office for more details
Coach Parking:	Yes. Coaches may drive up to entrance and unload before parking at beach.
	Limited parking for small coaches by entrance.
Length of Visit:	At least 2 hours for garden and 1 hour for house
Booking Contact:	Cheryl Kufel, Estate Office, Caerhays, St Austell, Cornwall PL26 6LY
	Tel: 01872 500025 Fax: 01872 501870
e-mail:	enquiries@caerhays.co.uk
Website:	www.caerhays.co.uk
Location:	South Cornwall coast between Mevagissey and Portloe, 9 m SW of St Austell

Please quote this guide when making a booking

Enys is considered to be the oldest garden in Cornwall. Robert de Enys lived there during the reign of Edward 1. The 1709 edition of Camden's Magna Britannia mentioned that Enys was noted for its fine gardens.

One of the main features is the Ladies Garden, later called the Flower Garden. This garden leads in to the Colonel's Garden, named after Colonel Enys (1757 -1818).

J D Enys, an inveterate traveller, greatly enriched Enys with seeds and plants he regularly sent home from New Zealand and Patagonia.

In spring the bluebells in the parkland, known as Parc Lye, are a sight to behold. This area is believed to be undisturbed since ancient times.

Probably the most valuable asset to the garden is its microclimate together with its peaceful and tranquil setting.

Fact File

Opening Times:	Tuesdays, Thursdays, and the first Sunday of the month from 2 p.m., 1st April to 30th Sept.
Admission Rates:	Adults: £4.00, Senior Citizens: £3.00, Children and students: £1.00.
Facilities:	Teas.
Disabled Access:	Yes, wheelchair loan available.
Toilets on site:	Yes.
Tours/Events:	Guided tours available, booking required.
Coach Parking:	Yes.
Car Parking on site:	Yes.
Length of Visit:	1-2 hours.
Booking Contact:	Danielle Dixon
	Enys Gardens, St Gluvias, Penryn, Cornwall
	Telephone: 01326 259885 or 07770 662849
	Fax: 01872 223421
Email:	whwone@supanet.com
Website:	www.enystrust.org.uk
Location:	Off Truro to Falmouth road, A39.
	From Truro: 2nd left after Norway Inn. Follow signs.
	From Falmouth: to Penryn (B3292). At Cross Keys pub, right fork into Truro Hill and follow signs.

.

Please quote this guide when making a booking

Lose yourself in the Nation's Favourite Garden (BBC poll), celebrating their 21st anniversary of being rediscovered. Uncovered from decades of overgrowth the mysterious gardens and estate today offer over 200 acres for exploration.

Discover the finest Productive Gardens in Britain and romantic Pleasure Grounds, along winding paths, laid out over two centuries ago. Step back in time and journey across the world beneath historic rhododendron boughs in Sikkim, past Maori-carved tree ferns from New Zealand, to explore our Italian Garden and Alpine inspired Ravine.

Get lost in our exotic Jungle whilst adventuring along raised boardwalks past giant rhubarb, banana plantations and through tunnels of towering bamboo.

Ancient woodlands and pastures are managed to promote wildlife, which is celebrated at our pioneering Wildlife Project, offering an intimate view of native fauna.

Find yourself at The Lost Gardens and experience the magical atmosphere of the most visited private garden in Britain, inspiring your horticultural and wildlife interests.

Fact File

Opening Times: From 10am daily, all year round. (Except Christmas Eve and Christmas Day).

Admission Rates: Adults £10.00, Senior Citizens £9.00, Child £6.00, Family (2 adults and 3 children) £27.00

Groups Rates: Minimum group size 20, prior booking is essential.
Adults £8.00, Senior Citizens £7.00, Child £6.00. Pre-booked guided tour additional £1pp.
Note - these are subject to change in 2011.

Facilities: Licensed Tea Rooms, Lunchtime Servery, Heligan Shop and Plant Sales, Lobbs Farm Shop.
No Dogs April - September incl.

Disabled Access: Yes. All facilities and throughout most of the garden restoration and wildlife hide.
Wheelchairs are available on a first come first served basis. Contact us for information in various formats.

Tours/Events: Please telephone for seasonal details or see our website.

Coach Parking: Yes, by prior arrangement.

Length of Visit: At least 4 hours

Booking Contact: Group Bookings Department.
The Lost Gardens of Heligan, Pentewan, St Austell, Cornwall, PL26 6EN.
Telephone: 01726 845120   Fax: 01726 845101

Email: info@heligan.com

Website: www.heligan.com

Location: From St Austell, take the Mevagissey Road (B3273) and follow the brown tourist signs to "The Lost Gardens of Heligan".

Please quote this guide when making a booking

Pencarrow, the much-loved home of the Moiesworth-St Aubyn family for nearly 500 years, is set in 50 acres of Grade II* woodland and garden where dogs and children are most welcome.

Superb specimen conifers from around the world tower over a profusion of azaleas, magnolias and camellias galore, with 700 varieties of rhododendron adding to the blaze of spring colour; blue hydrangeas line the mile-long carriage drive throughout the summer.

Start exploring and you'll find a surprise around every corner – ancient Celtic cross, a 2, 000 year old Iron Age hill fort, Victorian lake and ice house, grotto, restful Italian gardens with fountain and an enormous rockery that was once the largest in the country.

The Georgian house boasts an impressive library with secret door (think of Harry Potter meets Narnia), elegant but "lived in" reception rooms, period bedrooms and collections of family prams, dolls, oriental porcelain, fascinating antique furniture and portraits.

Fact File

Opening times:	Gardens: daily 10.00 – 5.30 from March 1st – October 31st. House, café and shop: Sunday – Thursday inclusive: 11 a.m. – 5 p.m. from 3 April – 29 September (last tour of house at 3 p.m.)
Admission Rates:	Adults: House: £8.50, Gardens: £4.00, Senior Citizens: £8.50, Gardens: £4.00, Children: House: £4.00 Gardens: £1.00. Under 5s: free Historic Houses Association Members Free
Group Rates:	Minimum Group Size: 20. Adults: from £7.00, Senior Citizens: £7.00 Children: Please contact administrator
Facilities:	Shop, Plant Sales, Teas
Disabled Access:	Yes (partly). Wheelchair loan available – booking required
Toilets on site:	Yes
Car Parking on site:	Yes
Coach Parking:	Yes
Guided Tours:	Yes, booking required on arrival at house.
Length of Visit:	House: 1 hour; gardens 2+ hours
Special Events:	Please see website for craft fairs, outdoor theatre etc.
Booking Contact:	Jo Goode, Pencarrow, Washaway, Bodmin, Cornwall PL30 3AG Booking Tel No.01208 841369, Booking Fax No. 01208 841722
Email:	info@pencarrow.co.uk
Website:	www.pencarrow.co.uk
Location:	4 miles north of Bodmin on A389

Please quote this guide when making a booking

Trewidden Garden Cornwall

Trewidden Garden is steeped in history as well as natural beauty. Originally planted by Edward Bolitho in 1849 and then continued by his son T.B.Bolitho, the garden was considered the finest in the far west by 1906. The mild location, nourishing rainfall and south facing aspect all conspire to make the 15 acre garden an unforgettable orchestra of colour throughout the year and particularly during the spring months.

As well as the magnificent Tree Fern Dell which is set within ancient tin workings, you can enjoy one of its finest collections of Camellias and Magnolias in the country. Trewidden is a wonderfully peaceful and natural garden with a maze of paths and surprises at every turn. Tender, rare and unusual plantings together with water features, specimen and champion trees and artefacts from Cornwall's tin industry provide a wide range of interest for all.

Fact File

Opening times:	16th February – 2nd October, Wednesday – Sunday (open Bank Holiday Mondays), July & August open daily 10.30am – 5.30pm (4.30pm last admission)
Admission Rates:	Adults £5.50, Senior Citizens £5.50, Children under 16 - Free
Group Rates:	Minimum Group Over 20 – Adults £5.00, Senior Citizens £5.00
Facilities:	Teas, Plant Sales, Shop
Disabled Access:	Partial
Toilets on Site:	Yes
Car Parking:	Yes
Coach Parking:	Yes – Narrow access please phone for details
Wheelchair Loan:	N/A
Length of Visit:	1-2 hours
Special Events:	Charity open days and resident artist open days refer to website for details
Booking Contact:	Heather Baker
	Trewidden Garden, Buryas Bridge, Penzance, Cornwall, TR20 8TT
	Telephone: 01736 366800/351979 Fax: 01736 368142
Email:	Richard.m@trewiddengarden.co.uk
Website:	www.trewiddengarden.co.uk
Location:	Two miles west of Penzance on the A30 towards Lands End

Please quote this guide when making a booking

Trewithen Gardens   Cornwall

Trewithen means 'house of the trees' and the name truly describes this fine early Georgian house in its splendid setting of wood and parkland.

Country Life described the house as 'one of the outstanding West Country houses of the 18th century' and Penelope Hobhouse has described the garden as 'perhaps the most beautiful woodland garden in England'.

2004 was the 100th year in which George Johnstone inherited Trewithen and started developing the gardens as we know them today. The great glade on the south side is a masterpiece of landscape gardening and is a monument to the genius of George Johnstone. These gardens covering some thirty acres are renowned for their magnificent collection of camellias, rhododendrons, magnolias and many rare trees and shrubs which are seldom found elsewhere in Britain. The extensive woodland gardens are surrounded by traditional landscaped parkland.

Fact File

Opening Times:	Open 1st March to 30th September, 10am to 4.30pm Monday to Saturday. Sundays (March to May only).
Admission Rates:	Adults £7.50
Groups Rate:	Minimum group size: 20
	Group £5.00
Facilities:	Trewithen Tea Shop, Plant Sales, Camera Obscura, Viewing Platforms.
Disabled Access:	Yes. Toilet and Parking for disabled on site. Wheelchairs on loan.
Tours/Events:	Guided tours available, prior booking is essential. Occasional special events please telephone for details.
Coach Parking:	Yes
Length of Visit:	2 - 2½ hours
Booking Contact:	Glenys Cates
	Trewithen Gardens, Grampound Road, Nr Truro, Cornwall, TR2 4DD
	Telephone: 01726 883647 Fax: 01726 882301
Email:	gardens@trewithen-estate.demon.co.uk
Website:	www.trewithengardens.co.uk
Location:	On the A390 between Truro and St Austell.

Brantwood Cumbria

Brantwood's gardens and estate are like no other. Mature Victorian landscape gardens lead to Ruskin's own experimental landscapes, to ancient woodlands, high Moorland and spectacular views. Completion of the Zig-Zaggy, a garden begun by John Ruskin 130 years ago, and the High Walk, a spectacular Victorian viewing platform, brings a total of eight gardens restored at Brantwood. Expect the unexpected and explore 250 acres of fascinating landscape.

Whichever season you choose to visit you are assured year round interest. Spectacular azaleas in springtime; a collection of ferns, herbs and colourful herbaceous borders in summer; the vibrant colours of autumn; or a winter snowfall can transform the gardens into a winter wonderland.

Stroll the paths, sit and marvel at the magnificent views. Whatever you choose to do, you will take home with you the discovery of John Ruskin's legacy and inspiration.

Fact File

Opening Times:	Mid - March to mid - November daily 11am - 5.30pm.
	Mid - November to mid - March Wednesday - Sunday 11am - 4.30pm.
Admission Rates:	Adults £6.30 / £4.50 garden only, Child £1.35
Groups Rates:	Minimum group size: 10
	Adults £5.95 / £4.20 garden only, Child £1.35
Facilities:	Shop, Plant Sales, Restaurant, Craft Gallery.
Disabled Access:	Partial. Toilet and parking for disabled on site. Wheelchairs on loan, booking necessary.
Tours/Events:	A wide variety of events await, please check website for details.
Coach Parking:	Yes but limited.
Length of Visit:	4 - 6 hours
Booking Contact:	Deb Middleton
	Brantwood, Coniston, Cumbria, LA21 8AD
	Telephone: 01539 441396 Fax: 01539 441263
Email:	deb@brantwood.org.uk
Website:	www.brantwood.org.uk
Location:	2¼ miles east of Coniston. signposted from Coniston.

Please quote this guide when making a booking

Winderwath is a garden of five acres originally laid out at the beginning of the twentieth Century. The mature trees including Wellingtonia, Cut Leaf Beech and Cedar, date from this time. Extensive work has been carried out on the rockeries and herbaceous borders since the 1950s. More recently the pond area has been opened up

There is now a large collection of Alpine and Himalayan plants, including Arisaema and Moconopsis. There are many rare and unusual perennials including a good display of Salvias. We are well known for the display of Aconites and Daffodils in the Spring. There is a working vegetable garden in the Edwardian walled garden with apricots, nectarines and peaches in the greenhouses.

We have a selection of plants grown for sale and also sell second-hand garden tools. There are picnic tables round the pond area where you are welcome to enjoy a quiet lunch.

Fact File

Opening times:	10.00 a.m. – 4.00 p.m. Monday – Friday. Saturday: 9 a.m. – 2.p.m.
Admission Rates:	Adults: £4.00. Senior Citizens: £4.00
Group Rates:	Minimum Group Size: 12
Facilities:	Plant Sales, Second-hand garden tools for sale. Toilets.
Disabled Access:	Partial
Car Parking on site:	Yes
Tours/Events:	Guided tours available. Booking required.
Length of Visit:	1½ hours
Booking Contact:	Jane Pollock
	Winderwath Gardens
	Winderwath, Nr. Temple Sowerby
	Penrith, Cumbria CA10 2AG
	Booking Telephone No: 01768 88250
	Booking Fax No: 01786 88250
Location:	5 miles east of Penrith on A66, Take B6412 to Culgaith and Temple Sowerby, from Temple Sowerby bypass, turn left onto old A66, 200 yards on right.

Melbourne Hall and Gardens Derbyshire

The historic garden at Melbourne Hall was designed by Rt.Hon.Thomas Coke in 1704. The pools, vistas and statuary are typical of the French style of garden fashionable in the 18th century. Robert Bakewell's magnificent wrought iron arbour is reflected in the main garden pool and the yew tunnel provides a shady walk way.

William Lamb, the 2nd Viscount Melbourne lived at Melbourne Hall and as Queen Victoria's Prime Minister he gave his name to the Australian City. The Hall is now lived in by Lord and Lady Ralph Kerr and their family.
Lady Ralph Kerr has initiated an imaginative and original planting scheme in the garden which includes specimen trees, shrubs and a unique collection of Magnolias and Roses, making this a garden of rare beauty and design not to be missed.

Fact File

Opening times: Garden, April – September (Wed, Sat, Sun, Bank Holiday Mondays) 1.30pm – 5.30pm.
Hall and garden – every afternoon in August except first three Mondays, Hall 2pm – 5pm, Garden 1.30pm – 5.30pm)

Admission Rates: Adults (Gardens) £3.50, Senior Citizens (Gardens) £2.50, Children (Gardens) £2.50
Group Rates: £2.50
Facilities: Visitor Centre, Shop, Plants Sales, Restaurant, Teas
Disabled Access: Yes – some areas limited
Toilets on Site: Yes
Car Parking: Yes
Coach Parking: No – none reserved
Wheelchair Loan: No
Length of Visit: 1-2 hours
Booking Contact: Mrs Gill Weston
Melbourne Hall Gardens, Melbourne, Derbyshire, DE73 8EN
Telephone: 01332 862502 Fax: 01332 862263
Email: melbhall@globalnet.co.uk
Website: www.melbournehall.com
Location: 8 miles south of Derby

Renishaw Hall is the home of the Sitwell family, as it has been for 380 years. Its eight-acre Italianate gardens, designed by Sir George Sitwell, were laid out more than 100 years ago, and are among the most beautiful in the country. There are several garden rooms, hedged with sharply-cut yew, and there is always the sound of moving water in the background, often reflected in still pools. On 28 February, we have our Fanfare for Spring, the only opportunity for visitors to see the structure of the garden at its best. There will also be specialist plant nurseries displaying and selling rare winter flowering plants.
From 22 April – 9 May Renishaw's bright bluebells are out in the ancient woods, with rhododendrons, camellias and magnolias in the newly-created woodland garden. 1000 roses bloom in June, which is the month the delphinums also reach their peak. The Laburnum Tunnel is bright yellow around the end of May, and later in the summer the herbaceous borders come into their own. Sir George's classical structure remains, but for the past year Head Gardener David Kesteven has been working with internationally-famous designer Anthony Noel, known for his dramatic design and use of colour and shape. Children can work off their energy in the new Fairytale Garden designed especially for them to play in and explore.

Fact File

Opening Times: Gardens open April 1st to September 30th 10.30am - 4.30pm. Wed to Sun & Bank Holidays. Hall: every Friday in the season.

Admission Rates: Gardens - Adults: £6.00, Concessions: £5.00, Children: £3.00, Groups £10.00, Tours: £6.00.

Facilities: New for 2011, Garden Exhibition, Café, Shop, The Sitwell Museum. The Rex Whistler Dinner & Conference Room. Wedding facilities available.

Disabled Access: Partial access. Disabled toilets and car parking.

Tours/Events: Group bookings (25+) available for The Hall Wed-Fri (ring for details – pre booking essential). Guided tours of vineyard and garden available.
Fanfare for Spring - 27 February. 27 April - 11 May: Bluebell Fortnight.
Other events all year (information on website).

Coach Parking: Yes

Length of Visit: Hall tour – 1 hour

Booking Contact: Administrator
Renishaw Hall Gardens, Renishaw Hall, Renishaw Park, Renishaw, Nr. Sheffield, S21 3WB.
Telephone: 01246 432310 Fax: 01246 430760

Email: enquiries@renishaw-hall.co.uk

Website: www.renishaw-hall.co.uk

Location: Junction 30 off the M1. A6135 to Sheffield/Eckington.

Please quote this guide when making a booking

Broomhill lies in one of the most glorious valleys in North Devon surrounded by hundreds of acres of woodland and bound by its own stream. The Broomhill Sculpture Park displays one of the largest permanent collections of contemporary art and sculpture in the South West. 300 sculptures by over 60 sculptors are sited in 10 acres of garden that present a wonderful balance between art and nature. The woodland gardens provide all year round interest and are home to numerous birds and insects. The gardens are full of colour in the Summer, Autumn and are particularly beautiful in the Spring, with successions of Spring flowers including Snowdrops, Daffodils, Primroses, Bluebells and Azaleas. The award winning Broomhill Kitchen is based around the 'Slow food' philosophy, where respect for authentic produce and local ingredients is paramount to our offering - pure celebration on a plate. Consisting of mainly Mediterranean cuisine using fresh, organic, fair trade produce from neighbouring farms and the coast, the menu affords splendid choice and excellent value. Group lunches and cream teas are available, served in our intimate restaurant or outside on the sun-warmed terrace. Special offer for groups of Ten and over: Mediterranean one-course lunch and garden ticket, £10pp (booking is essential) offer valid on week days only. If you fancy making an all-day trip to the area, the stunning Marwood Hill Gardens is only 10 minutes away from Broomhill.

Fact File

Opening times: Sculpture Gardens: Open all year (Mon-Sun) 11:00 until 16:00. Art Gallery: Open all year (Wed-Sun) 11:00 until 16:00. (Occasionally the gallery will be closed for short periods.) Restaurant: Lunch - Wed, Thu, Fri & Sun, Dinner - Fri & Sat (Occasionally the restaurant will be closed for functions.) Hotel: Open all year Mon - Sun. Please note: We are closed between 20 Dec and 15 Jan.

Admission Rates: Adults: £4.50, Senior Citizens: £3.50, Children: £1.50 (15 and under), Family ticket: £10.00 (2 adults + 2 under 15)

Group Rates: Minimum Group Size: 10. Adults: £3.50, Senior Citizens: £2.50, Children: £1.50

Facilities: Restaurant / Café, Sculpture Park & Gallery, Hotel Accommodation, Conference / Meeting Rooms, Event Venue, Wedding Receptions and Ceremonies. Available for purchase at Broomhill: Sculptures, gallery art-work, gift vouchers, postcards and art T-shirts.

Disabled Access: Yes, but limited. The restaurant, gallery, & terrace is accessible by wheelchair, the accommodation and garden is not. Disabled parking is available.

Toilets on site: Yes

Car/Coach Parking: Yes

Tours: Yes, booking required.

Special Events: Broomhill hosts a variety of exciting events throughout the year, such as art exhibitions, workshops, monthly Jazz concerts, lectures and food events. The Broomhill Art & Sculpture Foundation's National Sculpture Prize Exhibition opens in June 2011 (please visit our website for details).

Length of Visit: 2 - 3 hours

Booking Contact: Broomhill Sculpture Gardens, Broomhill Art Hotel, Muddiford Rd, Barnstaple, Devon, EX31 4EX Telephone: 01271 850262

Email/Website: info@broomhillart.co.uk - www.broomhillart.co.uk

Location: From Barnstaple, A39 towards Lynton, left onto the B3230 towards Ilfracombe. Broomhill is signposted 2 miles after the NDD Hospital

Situated in the rolling hills of Devon, Castle Hill Gardens provides a tranquil and spectacular setting for the elegant Palladian house built in 1730 by the Earl of Fortescue. Stroll through the 18th century landscaped garden with mystical temples, follies, statues and ponds and enjoy the Millenium Garden designed by Xa Tollemache with its striking water feature. The path then leads you across the formal terraces in front of the house where the eye is drawn to the distant Triumphal Arch. Wander through the woodland gardens, planted with rhododendrons, azaleas, camellias, magnolias and many fine shrubs and trees and finally down to the river at Ugley Bridge and the magical Satyr's Temple. The splendid castle perched on top of the hill has panoramic views to Exmoor, Dartmoor and Lundy Island. Finish your visit with a look round the recently planted walled garden.

Fact File

Opening Times: The gardens will be open from Friday 1st April 2011 - Friday 30th September 2011 every day except Saturdays, from 11.00am to 5.00pm, last admission 4.30pm. Refreshments available. Autumn colour walks every day except Saturdays in October and November from 11.00am - 4.00pm. Refreshments not available. Groups and coach parties are welcome at other times by prior arrangement.

Admission Rates: Adults - £4.50, Senior Citizens £4.00, Children under 14 free. Nature Trail Quiz 50p.

Group Rates: Minimum size 20+, Adults £4.00.National Trust members not free, RHS members not free.

Facilities: Teas and refreshments available, Groups and coach parties must pre order lunches and teas in the West Wing.

Disabled Access: Yes but there are gravel paths and some areas are only accessible by steep paths.

Tours/Events: Yes, booking required, time required - minimum 1 hour.

Events: Please see website for all events www.castlehilldevon.co.uk

Car/Coach Parking: Yes.   **Toilets On Site:** Yes.

Length of Visit: 3 – 4 hours

Booking Contact: Clare Agertoft, Castle Hill Gardens, Filleigh, Barnstaple, Devon EX32 02Q.

Email: gardens@castlehill-devon.com   **Website:** www.castlehilldevon.co.uk

Location: See website - Leave A361 (north devon link road) at roundabout signed South Molton onto B3226. Take second turning right signed 'Stags Head and Filleigh'. Shortly after passing through Stags Head look out for yellow lodge on right.

Please quote this guide when making a booking

This inspirational garden blends seamlessly into a timeless Devon landscape, and offers stunning views in all directions. The 8-acre garden is really several gardens in one, using over 6,000 varieties of plants to great effect in both traditional and naturalistic planting styles. A new 2-acre Arboretum will be started in 2011 to celebrate the Golden Jubilee of the Fortescue Garden Trust, which owns and administers this outstanding garden.

In spring – admire magnificent collections of camellias, magnolias and rhododendrons. Enjoy the Bulb Meadow with its masses of woodland plants such as erythroniums, anemones, cyclamen and bluebells.

In summer – experience the delights of the famous Walled Garden built around medieval ruins, wisteria bridges, the exotic South African Garden as well as the romantic Cottage Garden and Wild Flower Meadow.

In autumn – a glade of Japanese maples provide a kaleidoscope of autumnal colour.

Plant Sales has an excellent range of quality plants, including many of those grown in the garden.

The Garden Tearooms are situated in the former vicarage and serve delicious homemade cakes, Devon cream teas and light lunches.

Fact File

Opening times:	10.30 a.m. – 5.00 pm daily 1 March – 31 October 2011 Weekends only in February (Snowdrops and early spring bulbs).
Admission Rates:	Adults: £6.95, Children: £2.75 (5-16 years)
Group Rates:	Minimum Group Size: 10. Standard Rate: £5.80.
Facilities:	Plant Sales, tearooms serving lunches and teas.
Disabled Access:	Not all areas are flat. Therefore, limited disabled access.
Toilets on site:	Yes
Car Parking:	Yes
Coach Parking:	Yes
Guided Tours:	Yes, booking required.
Length of visit:	2 – 3 hours
Special Events:	A full events programme throughout the year. Please see our website or telephone for details.
Booking Contact:	Rachel Young, Administrator, The Garden House, Buckland Monachorum, Yelverton, Devon, PL20 7LQ. Booking Tel No. 01822 854769.
Email:	office@thegardenhouse.org.uk
Website:	www.thegardenhouse.org.uk
Location:	10 miles north of Plymouth. Signed off A386 at Yelverton.

Please quote this guide when making a booking

Hartland Abbey is a much loved family home, gifted by Henry VIII to an ancestor of the present owners. In a beautiful valley leading to an Atlantic cove, the house with its stunning interiors and collections is also open, making this the perfect destination in any weather.

Much of the 50 acres of gardens and grounds was lost under mountainous undergrowth from the outbreak of the First World War until 1996. Ongoing restoration has revealed the 'lost' Fernery and Bog Garden by Jekyll, winding paths through woodland gardens of spring flowering shrubs, hydrangeas and eucryphia, the Gazebo on the cliff and the Summerhouse, newly restored for 2011. Three romantic 18thC Walled Gardens once again grow herbaceous, tender and rare perennials, vegetables and fruit. Glasshouses protect dazzling displays of houseplants.

Snowdrops, historic daffodils and bluebells enchant early visitors. Enjoy walks to the beach and Blackpool Mill where 'The Shell Seekers' and 'Sense and Sensibility' were recently filmed. Welsh Mountain sheep, peacocks and donkeys roam the parkland. Delicious light lunches and home made cream teas are served in the Old Kitchens. Only 1 mile from Hartland Quay and 5m from Clovelly.

Fact File

Opening times:	April 1st – October 2nd 11.30am – 5pm
Admission Rates:	Gardens, Grounds and Beachwalk , Adult £5.00, Children £2.00
	House, Gardens, Grounds and Beachwalk , Adult £10.00, Children £3.50
Group Rates:	Minimum Group Size 20. House, Gardens, Grounds and Beachwalk , Adult £8.50
	For Group sizes 30+ House, Gardens, Grounds and Beachwalk, Adult £8.00
Facilities:	Light lunches and cream teas. Shop and plant sales.
Disabled Access:	Partial
Tours Events:	Guided Tours (optional) and Group Bookings by appointment.
Coach Parking:	Yes
Length of Visit:	(with house) 2½ - 3 hours, Walks and Gardens only 2 – 2½ hours
Special Events:	Snowdrop Sundays 6th & 13th February (11am – 4pm) Daffodil Day 20th March (11am – 4pm) Bluebell Days - Good Friday, Easter Monday, April 22nd, April 25th, May 1st & 2nd (11am – 5pm) Flower Festival June 17th – 21st
Booking Contact:	Administrator
	Hartland, Nr Bideford, North Devon EX39 6DT
	Telephone: 01237 441264/234 / 01884 860225 Fax: 01237 441264 / 01884 861136
Email:	ha_admin@btconnect.com
Website:	www.hartlandabbey.com or co.uk
Location:	15 minutes west of Bideford, 15 minutes north of Bude off A39
	via B3248 between Hartland and Hartland Quay

Created by Dr. Jimmy Smart – a fine plantsman. Marwood Hill has 20 acres of beautiful gardens and three small lakes set in a sheltered valley setting. A haven for trees and shrubs from around the world as well as herbaceous and alpine plants giving all year round interest and colour. The gardens are well known for the extensive collection of Camellias and National Collections of Astilbe, Japanese Iris and Tulbaghia. There are many areas where the visitor can rest, experience the tranquillity and enjoy the many inspiring aspects of the gardens.

The walled garden plant centre sells a wide range of plants, most of which have been grown and propagated in the gardens. Knowledgeable staff are usually available to help and advise.

The Garden Tearoom overlooking the garden offers a selection of light lunches, home baked cakes and Devon cream teas.

Fact File

Opening Times: Open Daily 1st March – 31st October.
Gardens, Plant Centre and the Garden Tea Room: 10am – 5pm.
Special openings in winter please contact us for information or check our website for details.

Admission Rates: Adult £5.50, Children (under 12) Free, Children 12-16 £2.50.

Group Rates: Group 10+ £5.00 Includes an introductory talk by Head Gardener. By appointment only.

Facilities: Visitor Information, Plant Centre, the Garden Tea Room

Disabled Access: Yes but limited. Ramped access to Plant Centre and The Garden Tea Room.
Please contact us for more information.

Tours/Events: Guided tours available. Events held. Contact the booking office for details.

Coach Parking: Yes

Length of Visit: 3 hours – all day.

Booking Contact: Mrs Patricia Stout
Marwood Hill Gardens, Marwood, Barnstaple. North Devon EX31 4EB
Telephone 01271 342528.

Email: info@marwoodhillgarden.co.uk

Website: www.marwoodhillgarden.co.uk

Location: 4 miles north of Barnstaple (Google map link on our website)

Please quote this guide when making a booking

Paignton Zoological & Botanical Gardens Devon

The 80 acre gardens of Paignton Zoo consist of mature shrubberies and newer areas developed over the past 10 years. The plantings are designed to create the feeling of natural habitats by using geographical and educational displays.

Themed areas include a Mediterranean climate garden, an economic garden and a medicinal garden. The Amphibian Ark water gardens, opened in 2010, feature seven ponds and interpretation about helping local wildlife.

Paignton Zoo's VertiCrop sustainable hydroponics installation is the first of its kind in Europe and the first in a zoo or botanic garden anywhere in the world. There are also three glasshouses which contain tender and tropical plants from around the world. The newest of these is Crocodile Swamp, which opened in 2009 and contains displays of tropical wetland plants.

The warm climate in the South West allows the Zoo to grow many tender plants outside. Palms, bananas and citrus are amongst the plants that contribute to the tropical feel. The Zoo is also home to the NCCPG National Collection of Buddleja and is working towards establishing a National Collection of water irises.

Fact File

Opening Times:	Open daily from 10 a.m. Closing times vary according to the season.
Admission Rates:	Adults: £13.10*, Senior Citizens: £10.80*, Children: £9.25*
	*Includes a 10% voluntary donation
	(These are 2010 prices, see website for 2011 prices or telephone 0844 474 2222).
Group Rates:	Minimum Group Size: 15. Adults: £9.90, Senior Citizens: £8.10, Children: £6.60.
Facilities:	Visitor Center Shop, Restaurant, Teas.
Disabled Access:	Yes. Bookable wheelchair loan available.
Toilets on site:	Yes.
Tours/Events:	Guided tours available. Booking required. Extra charge.
Coach Parking:	Yes - free.
Car Parking on site:	Yes - free.
Length of Visit:	4-5 hours.
Booking Contact:	John Rea
	Paignton Zoological & Botanical Gardens, Totnes Road, Paignton, Devon TQ4 7EU
	Telephone: 0844 474 2225
	Fax: 01803 523457
Email:	groupvisits@paigntonzoo.org.uk
Website:	www.paigntonzoo.org.uk
Location:	We are located on the A3022 Totnes Road, 1 mile from Paignton town centre.

Established in 1765 by the first Countess of Ilchester. Developed since then into a 30-acre grade 1 listed magnificent woodland valley garden. World famous for it's Camellia Groves, Magnolias, Rhododendron and Hydrangea collections. In summer it is awash with colour.

Since the restoration after the great storm of 1990 many new and exotic plants have been introduced. The garden is now a mixture of formal and informal, with a charming walled garden and spectacular woodland valley views.

Facilities include a Colonial Restaurant for lunches, snacks and drinks, a Plant Centre and quality Gift Shop. Events and concerts are presented during the year.
The Floodlighting of the Garden at the end of October (Oct 13th - 30th Oct 2011) should not be missed.

Fact File

Opening Times:	Summer: 10am - 6pm last entry at 5pm.
	Winter (November - February) - 10.00am - 4pm or dusk, last entry 1 hour before.
Admission Rates:	Adults £9.95, Senior Citizen £9.50, Child £7.00
Groups Rates:	Minimum group size 10
	Adults £7.00, Senior Citizen £6.50, Child £4.50
Facilities:	Colonial Restaurant, Gift Shop, Plant Centre.
Disabled Access:	Yes. 50% of garden accessible. Toilet and parking for disabled on site. Wheelchairs F.O.C.
Tours/Events:	£1 per person (minimum charge £20) on top of the group rate (minimum 10 people). Special events see web site.
Coach Parking:	Yes
Length of Visit:	2 hours
Booking Contact:	Jessica Lambert. Abbotsbury Sub Tropical Garden, Bullers Way, Abbotsbury, (Nr Weymouth), Dorset, DT3 4LA. Telephone: 01305 871130 Fax: 01305 871092
Email:	info@abbotsbury-tourism.co.uk
Website:	www.abbotsburygardens.co.uk & www.abbotsburyplantsales.co.uk
Location:	On the B3157 between Weymouth and Bridport in Dorset. come off the A35 near Dorchester at Winterborne Abbas.

Please quote this guide when making a booking

The 8 acres of gardens here hold National & International Plant Collections of Water Lilies, flowering from late spring to autumn, creating one of the most outstanding displays of water lilies in Britain with a Monet style Japanese Bridge as a centrepiece.

Many of the original lilies planted here by the Bennett family in 1959 came from the same nursery in France that supplied Claude Monet's garden in Giverny. These same varieties that Monet painted are among the collections on display.

Grass pathways lead you through the series of lakes surrounded by wetland plants, native trees, palms, wild plants and flowers. The gardens are a 'Site of Nature Conservation Interest' and home to abundant wildlife.

The Museum contains local history including Chesil Beach & Fleet lagoon, plus the fascinating story of this site from Brickworks & Clay Pits in 1859 through to the gardens today.

Fact File

Opening times:	April to September inclusive: 10 a.m. – 5 p.m. daily except Saturdays
Admission Rates:	Adults: £7.25, Senior Citizens: £6.55, Children: £3.95 (5 – 16 years)
Group Rates:	Minimum Group Size: 15. Adults: £4.75, Senior Citizens: £4.75, Children: £3.25
Facilities:	Visitor Centre, Shop, Plant Sales, Restaurant, Teas
Disabled Access:	Yes
Toilets on site:	Yes
Coach Parking:	Yes
Car Parking on site:	Yes
Guided Tours:	Yes, booking required
Special Events:	Please see website
Length of Visit:	2 hours+
Booking Contact:	Angie or James Bennett, Bennetts Water Gardens, Putton Lane, Chickerell, Weymouth, Dorset DT3 4AF Booking Telephone No. 01305 785150. Booking Fax No. 01305 781619
Email:	info@waterlily.co.uk
Website:	www.waterlily.co.uk
Location:	2 miles west of Weymouth on the B3157 – follow brown signs for Water Gardens from the A354 at Weymouth

Please quote this guide when making a booking

Forde Abbey is a treasure in an area already known for its outstanding beauty. More than 900 years of history are encapsulated in this elegant former Cistercian monastery and its 30 acres of award winning gardens. In the peaceful solitude of its secluded position it is possible to imagine just how it looked to many of its previous owners: monks going about their daily round of work and prayer, prosperous parliamentary gentlemen discussing the cavalier threat, gifted philosophers debating the imponderable, elegant Victorian ladies fanning themselves by the fireside and country gentlemen going about their work on the estate.

The architectural beauty of the house, with its striking interior, and the varied garden, including a mature arboretum, rockery, bog garden and working walled kitchen garden makes Forde Abbey a delightful destination. The cascade of lakes provides a wonderful setting for the Centenary Fountain, the highest powered fountain in England.

However, Forde Abbey is first and foremost a family home giving it an atmosphere of warmth and ease not often found in stately homes. The fruits of the garden and farm can be sampled in the Undercroft restaurant with a wide selection of delicious homemade lunches and cakes. A gift shop, plant centre and pottery exhibition add to the day.

Enjoy England Awards for Excellence, Silver winner 2008

Fact File

Opening times:	Gardens open daily throughout the year from 10am (last admission 4.30pm). House open, 1st April to end of October, 12noon-4pm on Tue -Fri, Sundays & Bank Holiday Mondays.
Admission Rates:	Tel: 01460 221290
Groups Rates:	Minimum group size 15, Tel: 01460 220231.
Facilities:	Shop, Plant Sales, Teas, Restaurant and Pottery Exhibition.
Disabled Access:	Yes. (house not suitable for wheelchairs) Toilet and parking for disabled on site. Wheelchair and Battery Car on loan, booking necessary. To book 01460 221699.
Tours:	Tours for pre-arranged groups only.
Coach Parking:	Yes
Length of Visit:	3 hours
Booking Contact:	Mrs Carolyn Clay Forde Abbey, Chard, TA20 4LU Telephone: 01460 220231 Fax: 01460 220296
Email:	info@fordeabbey.co.uk
Website:	www.fordeabbey.co.uk
Location:	Signposted from A30 Chard to Crewkerne & from A358 Chard to Axminster. 4 miles south east of Chard.

The National Trust Kingston Lacy

Laid out by successive members of the Bankes family over the last three centuries, the grounds of this extensive estate are presented by the National Trust in their Edwardian splendour. Most recent of the restoration projects is the Japanese Gardens of Henrietta Bankes, the formal Tea Gardens of which were opened in 2005, set in seven acres of the southern shelter-belt and include an Acer Glade, a Quarry Garden, an Evergreen Garden and a Cherry Garden. Closer to the magnificent Mansion are the Sunk Garden and the Parterre, both of which remain true to their early twentieth century planting patterns throughout the year. The Fernery, with over thirty-five varieties, is also the home of the National Collection of Anemone nemorosa, while the surrounding three hundred-acre Parkland reflects the Bankes' passion for specimen trees whether as single examples or as groups and avenues.

Fact File

Opening Times:	12th March – 30th October, Daily 10.30 a.m. – 6 p.m.
	3rd Jan - 11th March Daily 10.30 a.m. – 4 p.m.
	31st Oct - 23rd Dec Daily 10.30 a.m. – 4 p.m.
Admission Rates:	Gardens Only: Adults: £6.00, Children: £3.00. Includes a voluntary donation but visitors can choose to pay the standard prices displayed at the property and on the website.
Group Rates:	Minimum Groups Size: 15
	Group rates for House and Gardens only: Adults: £10.00, Children: £5.00.
Facilities:	Woodland Walks, Children's play areas.
Disabled Access:	Yes – gardens only. Lavatory and car parking on site. Wheelchair Loan booking available.
Tours/Events:	Guided tours available. Events leaflet available.
Coach Parking:	Yes – booking essential.
Length of Visit:	2 hours +
Booking Contact:	Carol Dougherty, Property Administrator, Kingston Lacy, Wimborne Minster, Dorset BH21 4EA Telephone: 01202 883402 Fax: 01202 882402
Email:	kingstonlacy@nationaltrust.org.uk
Website:	www.nationaltrust.org.uk
Location:	1½ miles west of Wimborne Minster, on B3082.

Please quote this guide when making a booking

Kingston Maurward Gardens & Animal Park Dorset

Set in idyllic surroundings Kingston Maurward Gardens are one of Dorset's best kept secrets. A tranquil, and peaceful spot, the gardens are situated in undulating Dorset countryside, with a large ornamental lake, broad sweeping and formal gardens.

The gardens were laid out in the "Jardin Anglais" style popularised by Capability Brown in the 18th Century. The formal gardens consist of a matrix of small gardens each with its own theme. The Rainbow beds and beautiful herbaceous borders compliment the Croquet lawn and an extensive display of tender perennials. The charming Japanese style garden lies adjacent to the north shore of the lake, with stately Chusan Palms, Bamboos and Japanese Maples. There are also tree trails, lakeside walks and a delightful walled garden.

The Animal Park has an interesting collection of animals, including Rabbits, Guinea Pigs, Sheep, Goats, Shetland ponies, Alpacas and lots more. There is plenty of space for picnics and the Visitor Centre has a wide variety of plants and gifts for sale.

Fact File

Opening times: 4th January 2011 to 22nd December 2011, 10am - 5.30pm.
Admission Rates: Adults £5.00, Senior Citizen £4.50, Child £3.00, Family £15.50.
Group Rates: Minimum group size: 10
Adults £4.50, Senior Citizen £4.50, Child £3.00.
Facilities: Visitor Centre, Shop, Tea Room, Plant Sales, Picnic Area
Children's Play Area, Animal Park.
Disabled Access: Yes. Toilet & parking for disabled on site. Wheelchairs on loan, booking necessary.
Tours/Events: Guided walks are available if booked in advance.
Special events take place throughout the year, telephone for details.
Coach Parking: Yes
Length of Visit: Minimum 2 hours
Booking Contact: Ginny Rolls
Kingston Maurward, Dorchester, Dorset, DT2 8PY
Telephone 01305 215003 Fax: 01305 215001
Email: events@kmc.ac.uk
Website: www.kmc.ac.uk/gardens
Location: Signposted from the roundabout at the eastern end of the
Dorchester by-pass A35.

Please quote this guide when making a booking

Green Island Gardens

"A Little Piece of Heaven on Earth"

Green Island Gardens is a professionally designed Garden by owner Fiona Edmond. The site is a 20 acre triangular "land island" originally woodland now laid out with terraces, generous island borders, water gardens , a seaside garden, Japanese garden, gravel gardens and extensive woodland gardens all sensitively planted displaying many unusual plants, often of borderline hardiness thriving in the unique microclimate. There are many features that have been designed and constructed from materials found on site, mostly fallen oaks from the great 1987 storm, such as a tree house, decking and arbour spanning the pond and several timber houses along with numerous seats.

This is a garden for all seasons with plenty of interest all year round, from snowdrops in February, many unusual woodlanders in April, bluebells in May along with Azaleas Acers and Rhododendrons followed by the water gardens, mixed borders all summer and finally the spectacular Autumn colour.

Fact File

Opening Times:	February 1st – November 30th, 10am – 5pm daily
Admission Rates:	Adults £4.00, Children £1.00
Group Rates:	Minimum Group Size 20 – Adults £3.50, Children £0.50
Facilities:	Teas, Plant Sales, Garden Design Exhibition, Photographic Display of Wildlife Images, Toilets, Wheelchair Loan (booking required), Lunches (booking required).
Disabled Access:	Yes
Tours Events:	Guided Tours and Group Bookings by appointment.
Coach Parking:	Yes
Length of Visit:	2 hours minimum
Booking Contact:	Fiona Edmond
	Green Island Gardens, Green Island, Park Road, Ardleigh, Colchester, CO7 7SP
	Telephone: 01206 230455
Email:	fionaedmond7@aol.com
Website:	www.greenislandgardens.co.uk
Location:	From centre of Ardleigh, take B1029 towards Great Bromley. Park Road is 2nd road on right after level crossing.

Please quote this guide when making a booking

There is much to see in over 200 acres of gardens and arboretum throughout the year.

In the Walled Garden the five individual gardens and the longest double herbaceous border in East Anglia are a unique blend of traditional and contemporary, combining unusual landscaping and creative and colourful planting. The garden is at its best from early summer through to autumn but on the opposite lake bank there is the Millennium Walk, designed to be at its best on the shortest days of the year. Here stems of dogwood, rubus and birch reflect in the lake and the scent of Hamamelis lingers.

Each year new plantings mature, surprise and delight.

Fact File

Opening Times:	5th April-31st October Tuesday to Sunday & Bank Holidays 10.30am - 5pm.
	1 November-3rd April Fridays, Saturdays & Sundays 10.30am to dusk.
Admission Rates:	£4.00 Adult, Child £1.00 (5 to 16, under 5's Free), £3.50 Concessions.
Groups Rates:	Minimum group size 12
	£3.00 per person
Facilities:	Visitor Centre, Shop, Plant Sales, Tea Room.
Disabled Access:	Yes. Toilet and parking for disabled on site. Wheelchairs and buggy on loan.
Tours/Events:	Please telephone for details.
Coach Parking:	Yes
Length of Visit:	2-3 hours
Booking Contact:	Visitor Centre Manager
	Marks Hall, Coggeshall, Essex, CO6 1TG
	Tel: 01376 563796 Fax: 01376 563132
Email:	enquiries@markshall.org.uk
Website:	www.markshall.org.uk
Location:	Signed from A120 Coggeshall by-pass.

Berkeley Castle

Berkeley Castle is England's oldest inhabited castle and most historic home. Over 24 generations of Berkeley's have transformed a savage Norman fortress into a stately home full of treasures.

Successive generations softened the stern aspect of the Castle walls with flowers, until finally the present planting of the terraces was carried out with the help of Gertrude Jekyll at the turn of the last century. The gardens specialise in scent and the roses are a delight in June. Rare plants, shrubs and trees are to be enjoyed and a butterfly house.

From the Lily Pond, first built as a swimming pool during the time of the last Earl, sweeping curved steps lead down to the Great Lawn on which the remaining Culloden pine stands, said to have been brought back as a pine cone from the Battle of Culloden by the 4th Earl of Berkeley.

Today, the castle landscape remains largely as it was in the mid 20th century, but retains a sense of 'slumbering peacefulness' as described by Jekyll. This mellow old age is part of the castle's beauty and, visitors can ramble freely through the castle gardens and grounds, getting a sense of its long and eventful life.

Fact File

Opening Season: The Castle: Open from Sunday 3rd April - Sunday 30th October 2011.
The Butterfly House: Open from Easter (Friday 22nd April) - Thurs 29th September 2011.

Opening Dates: Open Thursday and Sundays and Bank Holidays in **April** (including Good Friday and Easter Saturday), **May, June, September and October** 2011
Open Sundays - Thursday during school Holidays (incl. all of July)
10th - 25th April 2011 (Easter), 29th May - 5th June 2011 (Whitsun Half-Term)
3rd July - 4th September 2011 (Summer), 23rd - 30th October 2011 (October Half-Term)

Opening Times: 11:00am - 5:30pm (last admission 4.30pm)

Admission Rates: Global: Adults: £9.50, Concessions: £7.50, Children (5-16yrs): £5.00, Family: 24.00
Butterfly House Only: Adults: £2.50, Children (5-16yrs): £1.50

Group Rates: Groups (25 or more): Adult: £9.00, Concessions: £7.00, Children (5-16yrs): £4.00
Joint ticket with Edward Jenner Museum:
Adults: £14.00, Concessions: £11.50, Children (5-16yrs): £7.50, Family: 34.00

Facilities: Visitor Centre, Shop, Teas

Disabled Access: Partial access only.

Tours/Events: Yes, see website for details

Coach Parking: Yes.

Length of Visit: 1.5 hours gardens. 1.5 hours castle

Booking Contact: Eleanor Taylor, Berkeley Castle, Berkeley, Gloucestershire GL13 9BQ
Tel: 01453 810332 Fax: 01453 512995

Email: info@berkeley-castle.com **Website:** www.berkeley-castle.com

Location: Just off the A38, midway between Bristol and Gloucester.
10 minutes from Junctions 13 or 14, M5

Please quote this guide when making a booking

Batsford Arboretum - The Cotswolds
Secret Garden and former home of the Mitford family.

One of the largest private collection of trees in Great Britain. Spring flowers, wild orchids and fritillaries. Amazing autumn colour. Waterfalls, a cave, giant Buddha and deer. A surprise round every corner

New from Easter 2011

New - The Garden Terrace Restaurant, serving freshly prepared locally sourced food throughout the day. Sit with spectacular views across the Cotswolds.

New - Gift shop selling gifts with a difference.

New - Garden & Plant Centre. A plantsman's paradise.

New - 5 acres of newly planted arboretum to explore.

Fact File

Opening Times: Open every day 9am - 5pm. (May close Wednesdays in December and January - Check before travelling long distances).
Also open Boxing day & New Years Day.

Admission Rates: Adults £6.60, Senior Citizen £5.60, Child £2.60.

Groups Rates: Minimum group size 20. Admission Rates less 10%

Facilities: Visitor Centre, Shop, Plant Sales, Teas, Restaurant, Garden Centre and Falconry Centre.

Disabled Access: Partial. Toilet and parking for disabled on site, wheelchairs on loan, booking necessary.

Tours/Events: Tours by arrangement. Events to be arranged.

Coach Parking: Yes.

Length of Visit: 2 Hours

Booking Contact: Mr Chris Pilling
Batsford Arboretum, Batsford Park, Moreton in Marsh, Glos GL56 9AB.
Telephone: 01386 701441 Fax: 01386 701829

Email: arboretum@batsfordfoundation.co.uk

Website: www.batsarb.co.uk

Location: 1 mile west of Moreton in Marsh on A44 road.

Please quote this guide when making a booking

Batsford Arboretum Is Growing!

© Portus & Whitton Landscape Architects, Cirencester

Throughout 2010 an exciting expansion and development project has taken place at Batsford Arboretum.

■ It includes the construction of a superb new entrance building which contains under one roof;

■ **visitor centre**
■ **garden centre**
■ **interpretation area**
■ **café/restaurant**
■ **shop**

■ Visitors to Batsford can enjoy all of these new facilities from Easter 2011, without paying the Arboretum entrance charge.

■ The Arboretum grounds are also being enlarged, so that hundreds of new trees and shrubs can be added to the collection.

■ This project is being delivered by The Batsford Foundation. A charitable trust caring for the future of the historic Batsford Arboretum and ensuring long-term public access to its nationally regarded collection of trees and shrubs.

If you would like further information about this project please telephone 01386 701441 or visit www.batsarb.co.uk

The Cotswolds' best kept secret! An award-winning three acre garden surrounding a fine 18th century Manor House and Grade I listed Tithe Barn. The garden features luxuriant terraces and wide herbaceous borders filled with stunning plant and colour combinations; imaginative topiary including a topiary walk, knot garden and parterre; water features including a raised basket pond from the Great Exhibition of 1851. Hidden away in a secluded corner is a unique Shade House filled with novel shade-loving plants. Throughout the garden, creatively planted pots add interest and colour and an 18th century raised walk provides an enticing link to the rolling Cotswolds hills beyond. Beautiful to visit in any season, Bourton House Garden also presents a magnificent late summer flourish when many gardens have run their course. The unusual, rare and exotic make this garden a plantsman's delight!
HHA/Christie's 'Garden of the Year' 2006.

Fact File

Opening Times:	April to October, Wednesday, Thursday & Friday – 10am – 5pm
Admission Rates:	Adult £6.00, Children under 16 Free
Group Rates:	April to October, Monday to Friday (but advance booking essential) Adult £6.00 (tour leader free)
Facilities:	Teas/coffee and homemade cakes in the Tithe Barn from June to September, Gift Shop.
Disabled Access:	Limited access for wheelchairs – 70%
Tours/Events:	Please see website for details
Coach Parking:	Yes
Length of Visit:	1½ hours
Booking Contact:	Christine Walford Bourton House Garden, Bourton on the Hill, Gloucestershire, GL56 9AE
Email:	admin@bourtonhouse.com
Website:	www.bourtonhouse.com
Location:	2 miles west of Moreton-in-Marsh on the A44

Please quote this guide when making a booking

Cotswold Farm   Gloucestershire

Cotswold Farm is a Grade II * listed Arts and Crafts house. Sydney Barnsley with Norman Jewson extended the 1720 Farm House for the Birchall Family in 1926. It is set in a stunning position overlooking a quiet valley with a Cotswold Garden on descending levels. The formal terrace, designed by Norman Jewson in the 1930's, provides a splash of colours for most of the year. The White Border now overflows with flowers, texture and scent. The informal shrub garden contains trees, shrubs and shrub roses. The Step Garden, now a Winter Garden, descends to the Bog Garden, which is at its best in May with primulas. Ruth Birchall's collection of named Snowdrops appear throughout in February, and are naturalized in the woods. The Walled Kitchen Garden is now six varied, colourful allotments full of fine vegetables. In May, June and July, native orchids grow in nearby fields.

Fact File

Opening Times:	All year round by arrangement.
Admission Rates:	Adults £5.00, Children Free
Group Rates:	As above
Facilities:	Teas by arrangement
Disabled Access:	Yes - Limited
Toilets on Site:	Yes by arrangement
Car/Coach Parking:	Yes
Wheelchair Loan:	Yes by arrangement – booking required
Length of Visit:	1 hour
Special Events:	Snowdrop open days – Sunday 6th & Monday 7th February 2011, 11am – 3pm. NGS Open Days Wednesday 15th & Sunday 19th June 2011, 2pm – 6pm
Booking Contact:	Iona Birchall, Cotswold Farm, Duntisbourne Abbots, Cirencester, GL7 7JS Telephone: 01285 821857
Email:	ionacotswoldfarm@uwclub.net
Website:	www.cotswoldfarmgardens.org.uk
Location:	5 miles NW of Cirencester. Off the old A417. From Cirencester turn left signed Duntisbourne Abbots Services, then immediately right and right again into underpass. Private drive straight ahead. From Gloucester turn left signed Duntisbourne Abbots Services, pass services; private drive on left.

Hidcote Manor Garden Gloucestershire

Hidcote Manor Garden is one of England's great Arts and Craft gardens. Created by the American horticulturist Major Lawrence Johnston in 1907, Hidcote is famous for its rare trees and shrubs, outstanding herbaceous borders and unusual plants from all over the world.

The garden is divided by tall hedges and walls to create a series of outdoor 'rooms' each with its own special and unique character. From the formal splendour of the White Garden and Bathing Pool to the informality and beauty of the Old Garden, visitors are assured of a surprise around every corner.

The numerous outdoor rooms reach their height at different times of the year, making a visit to Hidcote Manor Garden enjoyable whatever the season.

Fact File

Opening Times:	19th March - 30th October: Monday, Tuesday, Wednesday, Saturday & Sunday 10am - 6pm (last admission 5pm). From October last admission 4pm. Also open Thursdays & Fridays in July & August. Please call the property for further seasonal openings.
Admission Rates:	Adults £10.00, Senior Citizen £10.00, Child £5.00. (National Trust members free)
Groups Rates:	Minimum group size: 15 Adults £8.50, Senior Citizen £8.50, Child £4.25 (National Trust members free)
Facilities:	Shop, Plant Centre, Teas & Restaurant.
Disabled Access:	Partial. Toilet and parking for disabled on site. Wheelchairs on loan.
Tours/Events:	Please contact the property for a list of special events.
Coach Parking:	Yes. Groups must book in advanced.
Length of Visit:	2 hours
Booking Contact:	Lisa Edinborough, Hidcote Manor Garden, Hidcote Bartrim, Chipping Campden, Gloucestershire, GL55 6LR Telephone: 01386 438333 Fax: 01386 438817
Email:	hidcote@nationaltrust.org.uk
Website:	www.nationaltrust.org.uk/hidcote
Location:	4 miles north east of Chipping Campden; 8 miles south of Stratford Upon Avon & signposted from B4632 Stratford/Broadway road, close to the village of Mickleton.

Please quote this guide when making a booking

Kiftsgate Court Garden Gloucestershire

Kiftsgate is a glorious garden to visit throughout the seasons with spectacular views to the Malvern Hills and beyond. Three generations of women gardeners have designed, planted and sustained this garden.

The upper gardens around the house are planted to give harmonious colour schemes, whilst the sheltered lower gardens recreate the atmosphere of warmer countries. The latest addition is a modern water garden which provides an oasis of tranquillity and contrast to the exuberance of the flower gardens.

On open days plants grown from the garden are for sale. A wide and interesting selection are always available. The tearoom in the house offers delicous home made cream teas and light lunches in May, June and July.

"Winner of the HHA/Christies Garden of the Year award 2003"

Fact File

Opening times: May, June & July - Saturday to Wednesday 12noon - 6pm.
August - Saturday to Wednesday 2pm - 6pm.
April & September - Sunday, Monday & Wednesday, 2pm - 6pm.

Admission Rates: £7.00 Adults, £2.00 Children.

Groups Rates: Coaches by appointment, 20 adults or more £6.00 per person

Facilities: Plants for Sale, Tea Room, Gift Shop.

Disabled Access: Limited

Tours/Events: None

Coach Parking: Yes.

Length of Visit: 1 ½ hours

Booking Contact: Mrs Anne Chambers
Kiftsgate Court Garden, Chipping Campden, Gloucestershire, GL55 6LN
Telephone: 01386 438777   Fax: 01386 438777

Email: anne@kiftsgate.co.uk

Website: www.kiftsgate.co.uk

Location: 3 miles north east of Chipping Campden. Follow signs towards Mickleton, then follow brown tourist signs to Kiftsgate Court Gardens.

A place of tranquil beauty amidst fine formal gardens, Lydney Park is home to Viscount Bledisloe, and is steeped in history from Iron Age to the present day. In early season, the visitor to Lydney Park drives between a resplendent display of daffodils and narcissi, and beyond the car park are the Spring Gardens, a secret wooded valley with lakes, providing a profusion of Rhododendrons, Azaleas and other flowering shrubs. Discover an important Roman Temple Site and the site of a Normal Castle. Picnic in the Deer Park amongst some magnificent trees, and visit our museums, which includes a New Zealand Museum. Home made teas in Dining Room of House. Dogs welcome on leads.

Fact File

Opening times:	10am - 5pm Sundays, Wednesdays and Bank Holiday Mondays from 24th April until 5th June
Admission Rates:	Adults £4.00, Children 50p.
Groups Rate:	Minimum group size: 25 - Phone for group rates.
Facilities:	Tea Rooms, Roman Temple Site, Museums, Gift Shop, Plant Sales.
Disabled Access:	Not Suitable.
Tours/Events:	Tour of Garden can be made available.
Coach Parking:	Yes
Length of Visit:	1 - 2 hours
Booking Contact:	Sally James
	Lydney Park Gardens, Lydney Park, Estate Office, Old Park, Lydney, Gloucestershire, GL15 6BU.
	Telephone: 01594 842844 or 01594 842922 Fax: 01594 842027
Email:	mrjames@phonecoop.coop or reception_lpe@btconnect.com
Website:	www.lydneyparkestate.co.uk
Location:	Situated off A48 between Chepstow and Gloucester.

Matara Garden

Come and enjoy the tranquil beauty of Matara's meditative gardens and its dedication to the symbolic, spiritual and cultural role of trees.

It is an oasis from the stresses and strains of everyday life; a harmonious place where you can relax for pure enjoyment or reconnect with the natural world.

Matara is a haven for rare local fauna, endangered bees and butterflies. This year the skylarks have returned. What makes us special are our Chinese Scholar Garden, Japanese Tea Garden, Shinto Woodland, and a Celtic wishing tree. Meander through the many pathways, labyrinth, and a healing spiral and ornamental herb and flower gardens.

We aspire beyond horticulture and provide tree dedications, where people can build a legacy from marriage, births and memorial trees; all telling their own unique story tying visitors to the place and the place to visitors.

Fact File

Opening Times:	From 1st April – 31st October, Tuesday to Thursday, 11am – 4pm
Admission Rates:	Adults £6.00, Concessions £5.00 Children £3.00, Family rate - £15.00
Group Rates:	By Appointment, £5.00 per person. Minimum group - 20
Facilities:	We provide local, organic and seasonal lunches
Disabled Access:	Yes and toilet
Tours Events:	Enjoy a group guided tour; learn the history and walk the meditative labyrinth, healing spiral, and explore the symbols of the North American Medicine Wheel. Green Weddings, licensed and civil marriages and partnerships
Coach Parking:	Yes – At Hunter's Hall pub directly across from Matara Centre
Length of Visit:	2-3 hours
Booking Contact:	Holly or Rebecca
	The Matara Centre, Kingscote Park, Kingscote, Nr Tetbury, Gloucestershire. GL8 8YA
	Telephone: 01453 861050
Email:	Holly or Rebecca @Matara.co.uk
Website:	www.matara.co.uk
Location:	Kingscote Park is located approximately 20 minutes from either junction 18 of the M4 (12 miles) or junction 13 of the M5 (8.5 miles)

Please quote this guide when making a booking

Surrounding a very old watermill, and hugging the sides of a tiny valley, Mill Dene Garden really is hidden in the Cotswolds and is a place of beauty, tranquillity and rest.

The stream behind the house has an air of mystery with a misty grotto and shade plants. The herb potager has the village church as a backdrop and there are views over the hills to the Salt Way. The gentle sounds of water in rills and basins abound, as does scent, particularly along the Rose Walk.

The feel of the garden is light-hearted with the use of mirrors, trompe l'oeil, concealment and surprise apparently altering the boundaries and size of the garden. The owner, Wendy Dare, with help from Rupert Golby in the North Garden, has designed a highly individual garden. She started from nothing and, responding to the strong sense of place, has made a garden in the 'English Country Garden' style – the result is delightful.

Fact File

Opening Times:	Open April to end July, Weds, Thurs, Fri. Also open all Bank Holidays 2-5pm. See website for times of opening.
Admission Rates:	£5.50 adults, £5.00 concession, £3 Child under 15 with free garden trail. Season ticket: visit as many times as you like in the year: £20 single, £35 double Short 10/15 min talk can be given by the owner for individuals. Book ahead £10.
Group Rates:	£5.00 per pax. Min group size 20. Must be booked ahead. Short but entertaining talk £25.
Facilities:	Plant sales, light lunches and cream teas.
Disabled Access:	50%. No toilets for disabled. Ring ahead for reserved parking and for ramps to be put out.
Toilets on site:	Yes
Car Parking:	Yes - limited. Coach Parking nearby.
Length of Visit:	2.5 hours
Special Events:	Institute of Photography are running Four Seasons Photography Courses: Fri 11th Feb (snowdrops and frost): Thurs/Fri April 28th 29th (Start at 7 am or sunrise): Sat, Sun 4th/5th June. Ring 01225 325773 for information. Willow weaving. A RHS Recommended Garden event. Decorative plant supports on 11th April: Willow sculptures to take home on 16th May. Ring 01453 751010 for information. Open for Red Cross Feb 13th. NGS 10th April
Booking Contact:	Wendy Dare, School Lane, Blockley, Moreton in Marsh, Glos. GL56 9HU Booking Tel No.01386 700457
Email:	info@milldene.co.uk **Website:** www.milldenegarden.co.uk
Location:	Take the Blockley turn off the A44 at Bourton on the Hill only. Coaches follow brown signs, stop at 1st left turn behind village gates by School Lane, and unload, then park where directed.

Please quote this guide when making a booking

Misarden Park   Gloucestershire

This lovely, timeless garden, with spectacular views over both deer park and rolling Cotswold hills beyond, was created in the 17th Century and still retains a wonderful sense of peace and quietness. There are extensive yew hedges, including a notable yew walk, a Lutyens loggia hung with wisteria and a wide York stone terrace overlooked by a fine specimen of Magnolia soulangeana. Beneath the terrace splendid grass steps, fringed with campanula, lead to the South Lawn and an ancient mulberry tree, believed planted in 1620. West of the house, a rill with fountain and a stone summerhouse are recent garden additions to commemorate the Millennium. Beyond the rill a large walled garden boasts extensive double borders which have undergone a total re-plant over the last two years and now contain a wide range of roses, clematis, shrubs and herbaceous, all arranged in individual colour sections and planted to provide flower and interest from spring to autumn. Newly constructed raised beds for vegetables are the latest addition.

Fact File

Opening Times:	10am - 5pm, Tuesday, Wednesday & Thursday, 1st April - 30th September.
Admission Rates:	Adults £4.00, Senior Citizen £4.00, Child Free
Group Rates:	Minimum group size: 20
	Adults £3.60, Senior Citizen £3.60, Child Free
Facilities:	Nurseries Adjacent.
Disabled Access:	Yes. Parking for disabled on site.
Tours/Events:	None.
Coach Parking:	Yes
Length of Visit:	1 1/2 hours
Booking Contact:	Estate Office
	Misarden Park, Miserden, Stroud, Glos, GL6 7JA
	Telephone 01285 821303 Fax: 01285 821530
Email:	estate.office@miserdenestate.co.uk
Website:	www.misardenpark.co.uk
Location:	Follow signs to Miserden from A417 or from B4070.

Painswick Rococo Garden is a fascinating insight into 18th century English garden design. The only complete Rococo garden in England, it dates from a brief period (1720-1760) when English gardens where changing from the formal to the informal. These Rococo gardens combined formal vists with winding woodland walks and more natural planting. However Rococo gardens were so much more, their creators showed off their wealth and included features that were both flamboyant and frivolous. The gardens featured buldings of unusual architectural styles, to be used as both eye catchers and view points. These gardens became regency playrooms, an extension of the house to be enjoyed by the owner and his guests.

We are restoring the Garden back to how it was shown in a painting dated 1748. We have contemporary buidings, woodland walks, herbaceous borders, and a large kitchen garden all hidden away in a charming Cotswold valley with splendid views of the surrounding countryside. Visit our Anniversary Maze, or come in early spring to see our stunning snowdrop display.

Fact File

Opening times:	10th January - 31st October. Daily 11am - 5pm.
Admission Rates:	Adults £6.00, Senior Citizen £5.00, Child £3.00
Groups Rates:	Minimum group size: 20 (includes free introductory talk) Adults £5.00.
Facilities:	Visitor Centre, Shop, Plant Sales, Teas, Restaurant.
Disabled Access:	No. Toilet for disabled on site.
Tours/Events:	Several day courses - see website for details.
Coach Parking:	Yes.
Length of Visit:	2 hours
Booking Contact:	Paul Moir Painswick Rococo Garden, Gloucestershire, GL6 6TH Telephone: 01452 813204 Fax: 01452 814888
Email:	info@rococogarden.org.uk
Website:	www.rococogarden.org.uk
Location:	½ mile outside Painswick on B4073

Please quote this guide when making a booking

Rodmarton Manor Gloucestershire

Rodmarton Manor is the supreme example of the Cotswold Arts and Crafts Movement. The garden was laid out as the house was being built (1909-1929) as a series of outdoor rooms covering about 8 acres. Each garden room has a different character and is bounded by either walls or hedges. One "garden room" has 26 separate beds with a wide variety of planting dominated by yellow shrubs and roses. There is a collection of stone troughs with alpines as well a rockery with bigger alpines. Topiary is a feature of the garden with extensive yew, box beech and holly hedges and clipped features including some new topiary. The herbaceous borders are magnificent from May but peaking late June but with plenty flowering into September. Many different types of roses flourish in the garden including old fashioned well-scented ones. There is a walled Kitchen Garden which has other plants besides vegetables including trained apples and pears. There is a big snowdrop collection. Most people who visit Rodmarton see the house which has specially made furniture as well as seeing the garden.

Fact File

Opening times: 6th, 13th, 17th, 20th February from 1.30pm, (Garden only for snowdrops).
House and Garden Easter Monday 2pm - 5pm.
Wednesdays, Saturdays, Bank Holidays May - September 2pm - 5pm.
Private coach bookings also at other times.

Admission Rates: House and Garden £8.00 (5-15yrs £4.00). Garden only £5.00 (5 - 15yrs £1.00) (no dogs)

Facilities: Teas

Disabled Access: Yes. Most of garden and ground floor of house.

Tours/Events: Guided tours of house and garden available.

Coach Parking: Yes

Length of Visit: 2 hours for house and garden

Booking Contact: Sarah Pope,
Rodmarton Manor, Cirencester, GL7 6PF.
Telephone 01285 841253

Email: sarahpoperodmarton@yahoo.co.uk

Website: www.rodmarton-manor.co.uk

Location: Off A433 between Cirencester and Tetbury.

Sudeley Castle Gardens & Exhibitions   Gloucestershire

Sudeley Castle sits nestled in the Cotswold Hills, surrounded by 1200 acres of grounds, award-winning gardens and historic medieval ruins. Sudeley's glorious gardens are amongst the very best in England, from the centrepiece Queens Garden, billowing with hundreds of varieties of old fashioned roses, to the areas of bold planting surrounding the ruins of the 15th century Tithe Barn. Topiary features strongly in the Elizabethan style knot garden and the magnificent double yew hedges bordering the Queens Garden, planted in 1860.
St Mary's Church within the grounds is the last resting place of Tudor Queen Katherine Parr, last wife of Henry VIII; the church is bordered by the White Garden, featuring topiary trees of Katherine Parr and her faithful attendant Lady Jane Grey. The arbour and beds of the neighbouring secluded East Garden features are planted with white wisterias, oriental clematis and tree peonies. New for 2011 is the Herbal Healing Garden, introduced by Lady Ashcombe, telling the story of herbs used throughout the ages for culinary and medicinal purposes.

Fact File

Opening Times: Open 26th March to 6th November 2011. Daily; 10.30am - 5.00pm.
Please ensure you telephone or visit our website for updated information before visiting.
Admission Rates: Adults £7.20, Concessions £6.20, Children £4.20. Family (2 adults and 2 children) £20.80.
Group Rates: Group rates available.
Facilities: Visitor Centre, Plant Sales, Coffee Shop, Picnic Area and Children's Play Area.
Disabled Access: Limited - garden only. Toilet and Parking for disabled on site.
Tours/Events: Group guided tours available - must be pre-booked. Special events programme, please call for details. (Information may be subject to change, please call or check website).
Coach Parking: Yes
Length of Visit: 3 hours
Booking Contact: Group Bookings
Sudeley Castle, Winchcombe, Cheltenham, Gloucestershire, GL54 5JD
Telephone: 01242 602308 Fax: 01242 602959
Email: enquiries@sudeley.org.uk
Website: www.sudeleycastle.co.uk
Location: On B4632, 8 miles north east of Cheltenham.

Please quote this guide when making a booking

Westonbirt, The National Arboretum
Gloucestershire

Westonbirt, The National Arboretum, situated in the glorious Cotswolds, is one of the outstanding tree collections in the world covering an area of 240 hectares (600 acres). Westonbirt is noted for its vast range of stunning mature specimen trees.

A short walk from the original arboretum is Silk Wood, with collections of native, Asian and American species that in spring are carpeted with primroses, wood anemones and bluebells. There are in excess of 16,000 numbered trees, including the exceptional National Japanese Maple Collection, extended in 2006 by the newly planted Rotary Glade. Colour is best in May (rhododendrons, magnolias, etc.) and October (Japanese maples, Persian ironwoods, Katsuras etc.). The plant centre offers some rare and interesting shrubs and trees, especially Japanese maples, conifers and specimen trees. Westonbirt Arboretum is an inspiring place to relax, get back to nature and indulge your senses. You will want to return to explore time and time again…

Fact File

Opening times: 9 a.m. – 5 p.m.

Admission Rates: Adults: £6.00 - £9.00 (subject to seasonal variation), Senior Citizens: Concessions available Children: £2 - £4 for children aged 5-18, Under 5 – Free.
Annual membership from £24.50 (concession single). RHS members free at certain times

Group Rates: Minimum Group Size: 10, Adults: £6.00, Senior Citizens: £5.00, Children: £2.00

Facilities: Visitor Centre, Shop, Plant Sales, Restaurant, Teas, play areas for under 5s, play zones for up to age 10

Disabled Access: Yes. Wheelchair and Mobility Scooter loan available – booking required.

Toilets on site: Yes   **Car Parking on site:** Yes   **Coach Parking:** Yes

Guided Tours: Yes, weekend tours Easter - October and tours for groups. Booking required.

Length of Visit: 3 hours plus

Special Events: Main Events: Festival of the Tree, August, Enchanted Christmas, December, Dog Days, February, Live Music, June/July, many more smaller events all through the year.

Booking Contact: Helen Daniels, Westonbirt, The National Arboretum, Westonbirt, Tetbury, Gloucestershire GL8 8QS
Booking Tel No.01666 881200 Booking Fax No. 01666 880559

Email: helen.daniels@forestry.gsi.gov.uk   **Website:** www.forestry.gov.uk/westonbirt-groups

Location: From the south west, Wales and London – we are 15 minutes north of Junction 18 of the M4 (Bath junction) on A433
From Cheltenham, the north and Oxfordshire – go to Tetbury via Cirencester and follow the brown signs south on the A433.

Please quote this guide when making a booking

Capability Brown designed more parks and gardens in England than any other man before or since. The Cadland gardens are unique in that they are his smallest surviving pleasure ground and were designed in 1775 for a thatched cottage, a Fishing Cottage, on the Solent shore overlooking the Isle of Wight. Gravel walks wind among the shrubberies with peeps out over the water; the evergreens or 'shining greens' were a favourite of the period, often overlaid with roses and under planted with wild flowers.

More parkland and two walled gardens were added later, one has a glorious run of fruit houses, a tool shed with a collection of old tools and a plantsmen's parterre, a series of gravel gardens with rare, low-growing plants; the second contains the plant collection. For those with time and energy, there is a woodland walk with a collection of oaks.

A visit to Cadland and Exbury Gardens and Steam Railway, (page 66) just 35 minutes by coach away, makes a perfect day out.

Fact File

Opening Times: Not open to the public except for group visits by appointment only.
Weekdays 4th May to 29th July: 12th September to 19th October. 10.30-5pm.

Group Rates: Minimum Group Size: 20, £6.00 per person, Children free.

Facilities: Visits hosted by the owner and Head Gardener; home made cakes, teas or morning coffee by arrangement; wheelchair access to most of the gardens: free garden leaflets; dogs on leads. House also open by special arrangement only.

Disabled Access: Yes.

Toilet On Site: Yes.

Tours/Events: Guided tours available.

Car/Coach Parking: Free. Directions sent.

Length of Visit: 2-3 hours.

Booking Contact: Mrs Gilly Drummond.
Stanswood Farm House, Fawely, Southampton, Hampshire SO45 1AB
Tel. 023 8089 2039 or 07760 296922 Fax. 023 8089 3040

Email: gilly@cadland.co.uk

Website: N/A

Location: 16 miles South East of Southampton on Solent shore via A 326/B 3053

Please quote this guide when making a booking

Exbury Gardens & Steam Railway Hampshire

Visit the world-famous Rothschild Collection of rhododendrons, azaleas, camellias, rare trees and shrubs, in the heart of the New Forest National Park. Offering peace, relaxation and tranquility – a day spent at Exbury is a day spent in paradise. Created in the 1920s, the gardens extend over 200 acres of natural beauty that echo to the names of the famous plant hunters. The early spring Rock Garden and Heather Garden, daffodils, camellias, magnolias and primroses give way to bluebells, rhododendrons and azaleas, with colour and birdsong at every turn. The spectacle of the Azalea Bowl in May is not to be missed. The summer months bring cool and shady riverside walks, hydrangeas and showpiece exotic and herbaceous gardens. Picnic next to ponds with golden orfe, carp and dragonflies. Autumn arrives in a blaze of colour from waterside maples, sweet gums and dogwoods, and Exbury's National Collection of *Nyssa* and *Oxydendrum*. Discover fabulous fungi and be dazzled by Exbury's Nerines (jewel lilies) in the Five Arrows Gallery. Explore on foot, by chauffeur-driven buggy or travel on the Exbury Gardens Steam Railway on an exciting 20 min journey around the Yard Wood. Railway features include a bridge, tunnel and viaduct, whilst there is a new exhibition to explore in the Engine Shed, "The Dream That Became Steam."

Copyright Colin Roberts

Fact File

Opening times: 19 March - 6 November daily, 10am - 5pm last admission. Gates close 6pm or dusk if earlier. Please call for winter opening dates / Exbury Santa Steam Specials in Dec.

Admission Rates: Adult £9; Senior Citizen £8.50; Child (3-15) £2 under 3's free. Family £21 (2 Adults & 3 Children 3-15). Railway + £3.50 (includes tour of Engine Shed). Family (2+3) + £13.50 Rover ticket (unlimited daily travel outside of April/May) + £4.50.
Buggy tours (30/45 mins) + £3.50 / £4.00. "Exbury Experience ticket" £14 - inclusive of entry, railway journey, buggy tour and Tree Trail leaflet, and discounts based on a minimum spend in restaurant and gift shop. Available from early June onwards.

Group Rates: Minimum group size: 15 - Adults / Sen Cits £8. Group Organizer free entrance to Gardens & Steam Train. Coach driver incentives.

Facilities: Gift Shop; Plant Sales; Teas; Fully licensed Restaurant; Buggy Tours.

Disabled access: Yes. Toilets and parking for disabled on site. Wheelchairs available on free loan. Accessible carriages on train. Carers admitted free of charge on 1:1 basis to Gardens.

Tours / events: Guided tours of Gardens (including specialist interest) and "Meet & Greets" are available. Full listing of special events and exhibitions on Exbury website.

Coach parking: Yes, free. We endeavour to meet all groups on arrival.

Length of visit: 2 1/2 - 3 1/2 hours min, but between 4-6 hours in main flowering season, April / May.

Booking contact: Reception. Exbury Gardens, Estate Office, Exbury, Southampton, Hants SO45 1AZ. Telephone: 023 80 891203 Fax: 023 80 899940

Email: nigel.philpott@exbury.co.uk **Website:** www.exbury.co.uk

Location: Junction 2 west of M27, just follow A326 to Fawley, off B3054, 3 miles Beaulieu, in New Forest National Park. B&W signposted.

Please quote this guide when making a booking

Sir Harold Hillier Gardens is one of the most important modern plant collections in the world. Established in 1953 by the distinguished plantsman Sir Harold Hillier, the magnificent collection of over 42,000 plants from temperate regions around the world grows in a variety of superb themed landscapes set over 180-acres of rolling Hampshire countryside.

Open throughout the year, the Gardens offer four seasons of beauty, inspiration and discovery and includes 11 National Plant Collections, over 250 Champion Trees and the largest winter Garden in Europe.

A £3.5 million Visitor & Education Pavilion offers fine views of the collection and surrounding countryside and features; a stylish licensed restaurant for home-cooked meals, light refreshments and afternoon teas, open-air terrace, gift shop, events, exhibitions, concerts and workshops for all ages and interests all year round.

Fact File

Opening Times:	Open all year except Christmas Day and Boxing Day, daily: 10am - 6pm or dusk if earlier, open until 8pm every thursday in June, July and August.
Admission Rates:	Adults £8.25, Concession £7.15, (seniors, jobseekers, full-time students and people with disabilities) Under 16 years - free of charge.
Group Rates:	Minimum group size 10, £6.60 per person.
Facilities:	£3.5 million Visitor & Education Pavilion, Open-air terrace and restaurant, Gift Shop, Plant Centre.
Disabled Access:	Yes. Toilet and parking for disabled on site. Wheelchairs on loan and Mobility Scooters for hire, booking advised.
Tours/Events:	Pre-booked guided tour with Curator, Botanist, Head Gardener and Horticultural staff available by arrangement. Please telephone for details about Special Events.
Coach Parking:	Yes (Free)
Length of Visit:	2 - 4 hours
Booking Contact:	Group Bookings. Sir Harold Hillier Gardens, Jermyns Lane, Romsey, Hampshire, SO51 0QA Telephone: 01794 369317/318 Fax: 01794 368027
Email:	info@hilliergardens.org.uk
Website:	www.hilliergardens.org.uk
Location:	The Gardens are situated, 2 miles north-east of Romsey. M3/M27 (West) to Romsey town centre. At Romsey follow brown heritage signs to the Hillier Gardens off the A3090. Alternatively, the Gardens can be approached from the A3057 Andover direction.

Please quote this guide when making a booking

Nestling in a woodland corner of Hampshire is this ravishingly attractive 1720's manor house, where busts of gods, emperors and dukes look down from the walls onto two major gardens. The inner gardens, enclosed by eighteenth century walls, are all devoted to parterres. One is filled with water lilles, another of classical design with box topiary and a third enacts the whimsy of Alice in Wonderland with the story's characters in ivy and box topiary surrounded by roses of red and white. The main walled garden is planted in subtle hues of mauve, plum and blue, contained in beds that have been faithfully restored to their original outlines. A decorative potager is centred around berry-filled fruit cages where herbs, flowers and unusual vegetables are designed into colourful patterns. All this is surrounded by a second garden, a remarkable neo-classical park studded with follies, birdcages and monuments. A Paradise water garden. A Red Paeony Dragon Garden now join the Garden of the Five Bridges. West Green House was the first garden to have a whole `Gardeners World' programme dedicated to itself.

Fact File

Opening Times:	Saturday 23rd, Sunday 24th April then every Wed, Sat, Sun until Sept 18th
Admission Rates:	Adults £8.00, Children £4.00.
Group Rates:	Groups by arangement please telephone for details. 4th April to 19th September 2009.
Facilities:	Tea Rooms, Nursery, Garden Shop.
Disabled Access:	Parking for disabled on site.
Tours/Events:	Opera July 30 & 31, Aug 6 & 7, check website for details.
Coach Parking:	Yes
Length of Visit:	2 hours approximately.
Booking Contact:	West Green House, Thackhams Lane, West Green, Hartley Wintney, Hants RG27 8JB Telephone: 01252 845582
Email:	pip@westgreenhouse.co.uk
Website:	www.westgreenhouse.co.uk
Location:	10 miles north east of Basingstoke, 1 mile west of Hartley Wintney, 1 mile north of A30.

This 3 acre garden of beauty and interest throughout the year is set in the magnificent Herefordshire countryside and has been lovingly created by its owners, Daphne and Maurice Everett since 1984.

Manicured hedges and archways enclose garden rooms containing lawns, borders and island beds of shrubs and herbaceous plants, a formal *Gazebo Garden* and a romantic *Arbour Garden*. Near the house are the *Cider Mill Garden*, the *Lion Garden* and an unusual *Knot Garden*.

Grassy paths meander through a woodland area planted with camellias, rhododendrons, magnolias, pieris etc to the *Far Garden*, with its collection of tree and shrubs, and thousands of wild daffodils and cowslips in the spring, then on to the *Long Walk* bordered with spring flowering heathers.

A path through the colourful *Summer Heather Garden* leads to the *Laburnum Walk*, and an intriguing *Secret Garden* completes the garden tour.

Fact File

Opening times: 2nd April – 28th September, Wednesdays, Saturdays, Sundays and Bank Holidays, 12.30pm – 5.00pm

Admission Rates: Adults £4.00, Senior Citizens £4.00, Children £1.50

Group Rates: Minimum Group Size 20, Adults £3.50, Senior Citizens £3.50, Children £1.50

Facilities: Plant Sales, Homemade lunches & teas in award winning tea room.

Disabled Access: Yes (one step to toilet)

Toilets on Site: Yes

Car Parking: Yes

Coach Parking: Yes (by prior appointment)

Wheelchair Loan: No

Length of Visit: 1 – 2 hours. Guided tours by the owners – booking required

Special Events: Open for National Gardens Scheme on Sunday 5th June, 10th July & 21st August

Booking Contact: Daphne or Maurice Everett
The Garden at The Bannut, Bringsty, Bromyard, Herefordshire, WR6 5TA
Telephone: 01885 482206

Email: everett@bannut.co.uk

Website: www.bannut.co.uk

Location: 2½ miles east of Bromyard on the A44 Worcester road (½ mile east of entrance to National Trust, Brockhampton)

Please quote this guide when making a booking

The **BBC Antiques Roadshow** is showing off **Hampton Court Castle and Gardens** on 6th February on BBC2 with a Second Edition later in the year. This 'gem of a find' set in over 1,000 acres in the heart of rural Herefordshire, and dating back over 600 years to King Henry IV, is a 'truly must see'.

Voted 30 in 'The 50 Best Gardens', Independent, May 2010

The twelve acres of stunning gardens feature flower gardens, kitchen gardens (highly acclaimed), avenues, borders, island pavilions, canals and a 150-year old wisteria tunnel leading to expanses of sweeping lawns. The 1,000-yew maze, with a gothic tower at its centre, offers panoramic views and a secret tunnel leads to a waterfall in the sunken garden. You can extend your visit with a tour of the beautiful Medieval Castle. Followed by lunch or afternoon tea in the 1846 award winning Joseph Paxton designed Orangery Cafe, supplied by the organically managed kitchen garden, and complete with an orange bearing tree! It is a 'truly magical day out not to be missed'.

'Possibly the most ambitious private garden of our time... one of the most successful public gardens in Great Britain'.
Stephanie Donaldson, Country Living, Gardens Editor

Fact File

Opening Times: 2nd April – 31st May Open Tuesday to Sunday (plus Bank Holidays)10.30am – 5pm.
1st June – 31st August Open every day 10.30am – 5pm.
1st September – 30th October Open Tuesday to Sunday 10.30am – 5pm.

Admission Charges: Gardens: Adults £6.50, Seniors £5.50 (both prices include a free garden admission on a second mid-week visit). Children £3 Aged 5 – 16, under 5's free.
Family Ticket £16.50 (2 adults, 3 children maximum).
Gardens and Castle: Adults £10, Seniors £8.50 (both prices include a free garden admission on a second mid-week visit). Children £4.50 Aged 5 – 16, unders 5's free Family Ticket £25 (2 adults, 3 children maximum). Opening times and prices may vary for special events.
No dogs, except for assistance dogs.

Group Rates: Please apply.
On-Site Facilities: Gift, Flower and Plant Shop, Cafe, Private Dining Room available for Groups.
Disabled Access: Yes, wheelchair loan available. Booking required.
Toilets on site: Yes.
Car/Coach Parking: Yes.
Length of Visit: Not restricted.
Booking Contact: Ticket Office, Hampton Court Castle & Gardens, Hampton Court Castle, Nr Hope-under-Dinmore, Leominster, Herefordshire, HR6 0PN.
Telephone: 01568 797777
Email: office@hamptoncourt.org.uk
Website: www.hamptoncourt.org.uk
Location: Situated on the A417, 500 metres from its junction with the A49 between Hereford and Leominster.

Please quote this guide when making a booking

In Spring, snowdrops, wood anemone, and wild daffodils carpet the Rhododendron Wood. Following on, with around 50 species cultivars of rhododendrons and azaleas planted in the 1950's. Embothrium, Eucrypia, Enikanthus, Magnolia, Halesi and Styrax provide an interesting planting in this mature woodland setting.

In Autumn, Acer, Betula, Cornus, Euonymas, Quercus and Cercidiphyllum, provide wonderful colour.

The newly created Walled Garden contains 20 different geranium species, 14 digitalis species and cultivars (largely perennial) and 9 nepita species.

The Vegetable Garden is divided into 3 areas. Vegetable plots, pergola (covered with roses and clematis) and a newly planted area with spring bulbs and cherry trees. The herbaceous borders will hopefully be of interest to visitors throughout the season with euphorbia, peonies, Echinacea, crocosmia, perennial phlox and asters. Homemade cakes and tea are a perfect way to finish a visit to the gardens here at Kentchurch Court.

Fact File

Opening Times: April – September. Please ring to confirm opening times. 11am – 5pm
Admission Rates: Adults £5.00. Children under 14 Free
Group Rates: Same as above
Facilities: Plant Sales, Artwork, Tea room – group bookings by appointment
Disabled Access: Yes
Toilets on Site: Yes
Coach Parking: Yes
Length of Visit: 1½ hours
Special Events: Refer to website
Booking Contact: Mrs Jan Lucas-Scudamore
Kentchurch Court, Nr Pontrilas, Herefordshire, HR2 ODB
Telephone: 01981 240228
Email: enquiry@kentchurchcourt.co.uk
Website: www.kentchurchcourt.co.uk
Location: From Hereford take the A465(T) road towards Abergavenny. After ten miles, at Pontrilas turn left and follow signpost to Kentchurch. After two miles, just after the Bridge Inn, fork left. After a further half-mile the road bends sharp right down a short hill. Opposite Church, turn left through white gates and up drive.

Please quote this guide when making a booking

The Laskett Gardens are the largest private gardens laid out in England since 1945. They are the private creation over thirty years of the historian, writer and diarist Sir Roy Strong and his late wife the designer Julia Trevelyan Oman.

Stretching over four acres there are some twenty different and contrasting rooms, including a rose garden, a knot garden, an orchard, a pleached lime avenue, parterres as well as a kitchen garden. It is celebrated for the orchestration of surprise and its thrilling theatrical vistas.

This is the Sissinghurst of the late twentieth century, a joint creation by two people who were at the centre of the arts in England embracing theatre, opera, ballet, films, museums, exhibitions, garden design as well as writing. What makes this garden utterly unique is that its makers wove the story of their marriage and their lives into its very fabric.

Fact File

Opening times:	Tuesdays and Thursdays to pre-booked, pre-paid groups April 5th to July 21st and September 6th – October 6th
Admission Rates:	Adults £10.00
Group Rates:	Minimum Group Size 20, Maximum 50
Facilities:	A small shop selling items exclusive to The Laskett Gardens. Only plants grown in the garden are sold. Recommendations of local places to eat available.
Disabled Access:	Limited but possible
Toilets on Site:	1 Unisex
Coach Parking:	Coaches for up to 30. Those containing more can set down, collect and park nearby.
Length of Visit:	1½ - 2 hours
Special Events:	Included in the admission charge is a detailed souvenir map of the gardens
Booking Contact:	Fiona Fyshe
	The Laskett, Much Birch, Herefordshire, HR2 8HZ
	Telephone: 07989 338217
Email:	info@thelaskettgardens.co.uk
Website:	www.thelaskettgardens.co.uk
Location:	Just off the A49 midway between Ross-on-Wye and Hereford. Details on website

Please quote this guide when making a booking

Moors Meadow Garden & Nursery

This highly imaginative organic 7-acre garden will fill you with inspiration and ideas and show you how to work with nature instead of fight against it. Set in rural Herefordshire up a winding lane and overlooking the beautiful Kyre Valley it is full of peace and tranquillity and a haven for wildlife.

The meandering paths will lead you through extensive shrubberies, fernery, grass garden and spring garden, into dingles, meadow with numerous specimen trees, shrubs and countless bulbs, past ponds and pools and herbaceous beds and borders.

Wander into cottage-style gardens, herb garden and large kitchen garden. The whole garden is brimming with rarely seen plants from around the world.

Ponder over the intriguing features and sculptures and relax on the unique home-crafted seats, meet the eccentric plantswomen. Featured on Gardeners World TV and voted the "Most Romantic" garden in Central England 2010 this garden is a "Must See"

Fact File

Opening times:	Friday - Tuesday 11.00 a.m. – 5.00 p.m.
	25th March – 7th September. If you would like to visit any other time, please ring.
Admission Rates:	Adults: £4.00, Senior Citizens: £4.00, Children: £1.00
Group Rates:	Minimum Group Size: 10. Adults: £4.00, Senior Citizens: £4.00, Children: £1.00
	(Includes free introductory talk)
Facilities:	Plant Sales. All the plants in the nursery are propagated from the garden.
	Artist, Blacksmiths, Picnics welcome.
Disabled Access:	Yes – very limited wheelchair access
Toilets on site:	Yes
Car Parking on site:	Yes
Coach Parking:	Yes, by prior arrangement
Guided Tours:	Yes, booking required. Guided tours conducted by the Head Gardener, subject to availability.
Length of Visit:	2 hours +
Booking Contact:	Ros Bissell, Moors Meadow Garden & Nursery, Collington, Bromyard, Herefordshire, HR7 4LZ
	Booking Tel No.01885 410318 / 07812 041179
Email:	moorsmeadow@hotmail.co.uk
Website:	www.moorsmeadow.co.uk
Location:	4 miles North Bromyard, 6 miles South Tenbury Wells on B4214,
	half mile up lane – follow yellow arrows

Please quote this guide when making a booking

Situated in the heart of the rolling Kent countryside, Great Comp is an exceptionally beautiful 7-acre garden surrounding an early 17th century manor. The skilful design of sweeping lawns, winding woodland paths and formal areas near the house entices the visitor to explore around the next corner.

Romantic ruins combine with luxuriant planting to great effect, allowing panoramic views of the garden whilst creating the perfect microclimate for the extensive range of exotic plants collected by the Curator over the past 15 years.

In Spring the garden erupts into bloom with numerous Magnolias, Azaleas and Rhododendrons, under-planted with large drifts of Hellebores and bulbs whilst Summer brings warmth and extravagance from the rich and fiery colours of Salvias, Dahlias, Kniphofias, Crocosmias and Fuchsias; these are punctuated with ornamental grasses in great variety.

Also on offer at Great Comp are delicious homemade teas and lunches in the Old Dairy and an eclectic range of choice and unusual plants from the award-winning Dyson's Nursery.

Fact File

Opening Times:	April 1st – October 31st 11 a.m. – 5 p.m. daily
Admission Rates:	Adults: £5.50, OAP/Disabled: £5.00, Children (6-16): £1.00
Group Rates:	£5.00 Minimum 20 persons.
	Season Ticket, Adults: £15.00, Senior Citizens: £10.00, Family: £25.00
Facilities:	Tearoom/restaurant, gift shop, nursery for plant sales
Disabled Access:	Yes, wheelchair loan available (booking required)
Toilet On Site:	Yes.
Tours/Events:	Annual garden show 13th and 14th August
Coach Parking:	Yes.
Car Parking:	Yes.
Length of Visit:	1-2 hours
Booking Contact:	The Curator,
	Great Comp Garden, Comp Lane, Platt, Nr. Sevenoaks, Kent TN15 8QS
	Booking Telephone No. 01732 885094
Email:	info@greatcompgarden.co.uk
Website:	www.greatcompgarden.co.uk
Location:	Great Comp is about 2 miles from Borough Green. Follow the brown signposts on the A20 near Wrotham Heath and along the B2016 and Comp Lane.

Please quote this guide when making a booking

WINNER - Best Tourism Experience of the Year 2005 - Tourism Excellence Awards.
There's magic and mystery, history and romance at this enchanting award-winning venue - which provides such an unusual combination of a traditional heritage garden with the contemporary landscaping of the ancient woodland.

First laid out in 1674 on a gentle, south-facing slope, the formal walled gardens are set against the romantic backdrop of a medieval moat house (not open to the public). They include herbaceous borders, an exquisite white rose garden with over 20 varieties of roses, a secret garden, knot garden, nut walk, paradise walk and oriental garden plus the drunken garden with its crazy topiary, and there's wonderful seasonal colour throught spring, summer and autumn.

In complete contrast, in the ancient woodland of the 'Enchanted Forest" there are quirky and mysterious gardens developed by innovative designer, Ivan Hicks.

Fact File

Opening times: Open Daily from 10am - 5.30pm April - October 2011

Admission Rates: Please see our website for 2011 dates and admission price information www.groombridge.co.uk or call the Estate Office on 01892 861444.

Group Rates: Minimum group size: 12
Adults £7.25, Senior Citizens £5.50 (off peak) and £6.25 (July and August - Peak)
Students £6.25, and Children (3-12yrs) £5.50.

Facilities: Gift Shop, Licensed Restaurant, Plant Sales.

Disabled Access: Yes. Toilet & limited parking for disabled on site. Wheelchairs on loan.

Tours/Events: Guided tours for groups - pre booked only, £30 per guide. Packed programme of Special Events throughout the season.

Coach Parking: Yes

Length of Visit: 3 - 4 hours

Booking Contact: Carrie Goodhew
Groombridge Place, Groombridge, Tunbridge, Wells, Kent TN3 9QG
Telephone 01892 861444 Fax: 01892 863996

Email: office@groombridge.co.uk

Website: www.groombridge.co.uk

Location: 4 miles south west of Tunbridge Wells on B2110, just off the A264 between Tunbridge Wells and East Grinstead.

Please quote this guide when making a booking

Managed by Bexley Heritage Trust, Hall Place is a fine Grade I listed country house built in 1537 for Sir John Champneys, a wealthy merchant and former Lord Mayor of London. Surrounding the house are award-winning formal gardens with magnificent topiary, enclosed gardens and inspirational herbaceous borders. In the walled gardens there is a nursery selling plants grown in the Hall Place gardens, and a sub-tropical glasshouse where you can see ripening bananas in mid-winter.

The house, which boasts a panelled Great Hall with Minstrel's Gallery, ornate 17th century plaster ceilings and various other furnished historic rooms, has recently undergone extensive restoration and was fully open to the public for the first time in 2009. There are new displays including an introduction to the house's history and exhibits from Bexley's extensive museum collection. The new visitor centre in the grounds offers a riverside tearoom and a gift shop as well as tourist information.

Fact File

Opening times:	Gardens open 9 a.m. – sunset throughout the year. Please telephone 01322 526574 for seasonal house, visitor centre and tearoom opening hours.
Admission Rates:	Free (except on special event days)
Group Rates:	Charges apply for guided tours and special events.
Facilities:	Free parking, Gift Shop, Plant Sales, Tearoom, Visitor Centre
Disabled Access:	Partial. Designated disabled toilet and parking on site.
Toilets on site:	Yes
Car Parking on site:	Yes
Coach Parking:	Yes
Guided Tours:	Pre-booked guided tours of the house and/or gardens available.
Special Events:	Extensive programme of events – please see website or telephone 01322 526574 to request a leaflet.
Length of Visit:	3 – 4 hours
Booking Contact:	Sue Pothecary, Bourne Road, Bexley Kent, DA5 1PQ Booking Tel No.020 8298 6951. Booking Fax No. 020 8303 6641
Email:	info@hallplace.org.uk
Website:	www.hallplace.org.uk
Location:	Black Prince Interchange of the A2, 3 miles from junction 2 of the M25, towards London. Nearest rail connection: Bexley. Buses 229. 492, B12, 132 to the foot of Gravel Hill

Please quote this guide when making a booking

Discover 700 years of history at this romantic double-moated 13th century castle, once the childhood home of Anne Boleyn and set in award-winning gardens.

The spectacular gardens are the masterpiece of William Waldorf Astor who between 1904 and 1908 created a garden paradise. Visitors can view the stunning topiary, wander through pergolas of roses, climbing shrubs and perennial planting in the magnificent Italian gardens. Absorb the breathtaking scent of over 3000 roses in the walled rose garden and tapestries of colour in the 110-metre herbaceous border or take a peaceful stroll through Sunday Walk in this quintessential garden.

Enjoy the yew and water mazes, grottoes, cascades and fountains, 38-acre boating lake or walk around Hever Lake Walk with splendid mature trees, splashes, waterfalls.

A garden for all seasons and perfect for weddings, conferences and special occasions.

Fact File

Opening Times: 21st February 2011 - 2nd January 2012. Gardens open at 10.30am. Castle opens 12 noon. February Half Term Holiday February 21st - 27th. Main Season (Wednesday – Sunday) 2nd - 31st March. Last admission 4pm. Final exit 5pm. 1st April - 30th October Daily. Last admission 5pm. Final exit 6pm. (30th October exit 5pm) Winter Season (Wednesday-Sunday). 2nd November – 24th December (See website for opening times)

Admission Charges: Adults: £14.00, Senior Citizens: £12.00, Child: £8.00, Family: £36.00 Gardens Only: Adult: £11.50, Senior Citizens: £10.00, Child: £7.50, Family: £30.50 Family Tickets (2 adults & 2 children or 1 Adult and 3 children)

On-Site Facilities: Restaurants, Picnic Areas, Shops, Plant Sales, Audio Tours

Disabled Access: Partial. Toilet and parking for disabled and a limited number of wheelchairs

Toilets on site: Yes

Car Parking on site: Yes

Coach Parking: Yes

Guided Tours: Pre-booked guided tours available of castle and gardens. Full calendar of special events.

Length of Visit: 4 hours

Booking Contact: Nicky Rees, Hever Castle, Hever TN8 7NG Telephone No. 01732 861701 Information Tel. No. 01732 865224

Email: mail@hevercastle.co.uk

Website: www.hevercastle.co.uk

Location: 30 miles from Central London. 3 miles SE of Edenbridge. Exit M25 junctions 5 or 6.

Please quote this guide when making a booking

Situated in the High Weald on the Kent and Sussex borders, Hole Park Garden is one of the Garden of England's best-kept secrets.

Spread over 15 acres is a garden for all seasons, set in the heart of the English countryside. Hole Park is located on the edge of the picturesque Weald village of Rolvenden. Hole Park has been owned by the Barham family for the past four generations. This outstandingly beautiful country house garden reflects the care and long-term planning that is unique to family-owned estates.

Formal, walled, meadow and woodland gardens are a feature and Hole Park is perhaps best noted for the extensive topiary, fine lawns and specimen trees and an amazing display of spring colour from the bluebells and rhododendrons, followed by stunning Wisteria and herbaceous borders.

Many visitors combine their visit to Hole Park Gardens with a trip to the historic Cinque Port of Tenterden, Sissinghurst Gardens or Great Dixter, only 6 miles distant.

Fact File

Opening Times:	All openings 11am - 6pm.
	Spring: 3rd April to 31st May - open daily (including renowned bluebell season)
	Summer: 1st June to 27th October Wednesdays and Thursdays.
	Autumn Sundays: 2nd, 9th and 16th October.
Admission Rates:	Adults: £6.00, Children: £1.00
Group Rates:	Groups are welcome at any time. Conducted tours and lunches available, please telephone for details. Prior booking essential.
Facilities:	Toilets, Plant Stall, Tea Room, Wheelchair.
Disabled Access:	Yes.
Tours/Events:	Bluebell & Spring Spectacular late April / early May inclusive.
Coach Parking:	Yes.
Length of Visit:	1½ - 2 hours.
Booking Contact:	Edward Barham,
	Hole Park Estate, Rolvenden, Cranbrook, Kent TN17 4JA
	Tel: 01580 241344 Fax: 01580 241386
Email:	info@holepark.com
Website:	www.holepark.com
Location:	4 miles south west of Tenterden, mid-way between villages of Rolvenden and Benenden on B2086

The National Trust Ightham Mote   Kent

Ightham Mote's 14-acre garden nestles in a sunken valley and surrounds the beautiful medieval moated manor house.

The North Lake Pleasure ground and ornamental pond were created in the early 19th century and are currently being restored to their former glory. Pleasurable views to the house show off its romantic setting. The sweet pea and lavender walk is a delight in late June /July. The Orchard, Enclosed Garden, Fountain Garden and Vegetable & Cutting Garden all contribute to the garden's sense of tranquillity for which it is famed.

The garden has "sat quietly" as a backdrop during the 15 year conservation project on the house. Now emerging out of the shadows for its moment of real glory, it is an exciting time to visit as the garden becomes an attraction in its own right. Changes will be interpreted for our visitors as they occur.

Fact File

Opening Times:	5 March - 30 October 2011, 10.30am-5pm (Last entry 4.30pm)
	March, April, May, September, October: Every day except Tuesday and Wednesday
	June, July, August: Every day except Tuesday
	For winter opening times please visit our website
Admission Rates:	Adults: £11.50, Senior Citizens: N/A, Children: £5.75, Family £29.00
Group Rates:	Minimum Group Size: 15
	Adults: £9.75, Senior Citizens: N/A, Children: £4.85
Facilities:	Visitor Centre, Shop, Plant Sales, Restaurant, Teas
Disabled Access:	Yes, wheelchair loan available. Toilet and parking on site.
Tours:	Pre-booked only.
Coach Parking:	Yes.
Length of Visit:	2 hours approximately.
Booking Contact:	Pamela Westaway, Ightham Mote, Mote Road, Ivy Hatch, Sevenoaks, Kent TN15 0NT
	Telephone: 01732-810378 Ext 100, Fax: 01732-811029
Email:	ighthammote@nationaltrust.org.uk
Website:	www.nationaltrust.org.uk/ighthammote
Location:	Between Sevenoaks and Borough Green, 1.5 miles south of A25

Please quote this guide when making a booking

Lullingstone Castle & World Garden   Kent

Winner of the UK's Best New Tourism Project Award in 2005. Set within 120 acres of beautiful Kent countryside, Lullingstone Castle is one of England's oldest family estates. The manor house and gatehouse – which overlook a stunning 15-acre lake – were built in 1497 and have been home to the same family ever since. In 2005, Tom Hart Dyke – 20th generation of Hart Dykes to live at Lullingstone – created within the Castle grounds a unique and inspiring 'World Garden' and filled it with thousands of rare, unusual and beautiful plants collected from all over the world (Tom came up with the idea for the garden whilst being held hostage at gunpoint in the Colombian jungle in 2000!) These plants, some 8000 different types, are now well established and Tom would like to offer your group a chance to join him on a unique and personal tour of the 'World Garden'. You will also have the opportunity to view inside his home – Lullingstone Castle.

Fact File

Opening times: April through September; Garden open Fridays, Saturdays, Sundays and Bank Holiday Mondays 12-5pm (except Good Friday). House open only for Bank Holiday weekends at same times, and for special events (see below) 11-5pm. Pre-booked guided groups for House, Church and Garden on Wednesdays and Thursdays by arrangement and for Garden only tours on Mondays and Tuesdays.

Admission Rates: Adults £7.00, Senior Citizen £6.50, Child £4.00, Family £18.00. Season ticket available (£20.00 for one year, £30.00 for two).

Group Rates: Minimum group size: 20. Guided groups £8.00 per person plus £40.00 per group for Tom or a dedicated guide. Unguided groups (during opening times): £6.00 per person.

Facilities: Toilets, book and plant sales, gift shop, refreshments (tea and cakes) during opening times or at visitor centre (10 min walk away). Picnics welcome.

Disabled Access: Yes. Toilet and parking for disabled on site. Wheelchairs available upon request.

Tours/Events: April free Garden Tours. May 15th Plant Fair. June 19th National Gardens Scheme. July 30th/31st Plant Hunters Weekend, August 20th/21st Salvia Weekend. September 9th/10th/11th Flower Arranging.

Coach Parking: Yes.

Length of Visit: 2-3 hours.

Booking Contact: Mr and Mrs Guy Hart Dyke. Lullingstone Castle, Eynsford, Kent DA4 0JA. Tel: 01322 862114 Fax: 01322 862115

Email: info@lullingstonecastle.co.uk

Website: www.lullingstonecastle.co.uk

Location: Off the A225 near the village of Eynsford and just 10 minutes drive from Junction 3 of M25.

Please quote this guide when making a booking

Tucked away up a Wealden lane lies an enchanting garden where planting and art blend to create a magical surprise around every corner. Marle Place is a peaceful, privately owned garden with ten acres of formal planting and many more acres of woodland. The delightful gardens are a combination of hedged rooms and tree lined avenues. Herbaceous and annual plants, and unusual shrubs give scent and colour throughout. The yew hedged kitchen garden includes a wide selection of vegetables, rose beds and an orchid house. The gardens consistently win awards for management for wildlife. The potting shed shop offers collectables, old and new, and the plant stand a large selection of perennials. Visitors are offered a selection of homemade cakes and teas in the quaint cart-bay tearoom. In the gallery there are exhibitions by contemporary artists. Artwork is also on show in the grounds, and there is an annual sculpture show in September.

We are proud to be one of "The Seven Wonders of the Weald" group of local attractions, web address: www.sevenwonders.org.uk and we are within 20 minutes of Scotney and Sissinghurst castles and the towns of Tonbridge and Tunbridge Wells and within easy reach of Hever and Penshurst castles.

Fact File

Opening Times: We are open: 1st April 2011 until 2nd October 2011 daily. Except Saturdays 28th May, 16th July & 23rd July when we are closed. 10am-5pm or outside these times by prior appointment.

Admission Rates: Adults £5.50, senior citizens and groups £5.00, children under 12 £1.50 and wheelchair users free.

Group Rates: Minimum group size 12. All adults £5.00, children, price on enquiry.

Facilities: Teas, Plant Sales, Gallery and Artist's studio

Disabled Access: Yes

Toilets on Site: Yes

Car/Coach Parking: Yes

Wheelchair Loan: Yes – Booking required

Length of Visit: 1½ hours minimum

Special Events: Events throughout the season. For full details visit our events section on our website or telephone for details

Booking Contact: Mrs L Williams, Marle Place Gardens and Gallery, Marle Place Road, Brenchley, Nr Tonbridge, Kent. TN12 7HS
Telephone: 01892 722304 Fax: 01892 724099

Email: lindelwilliams@googlemail.com **Website:** www.marleplace.co.uk

Location: Nine miles south east of Tonbridge off the A21. At the Forstal Farm Roundabout, take the B2162 direction Horsmonden. Follow the brown/white tourism signs, and then green Marle for 2.3 miles. From Brenchley village direction, which is 1.34 miles north of Marle Place follow brown/white tourism signs.

Please quote this guide when making a booking

Ancestral home of the Sidney family since 1552, with a history going back six and half centuries, Penshurst Place has been described as "the grandest and most perfectly preserved example of a fortified manor house in all England".

The 11 acres of Gardens are as old as the original house - the walls and terraces were added in the Elizabethan era - and are divided into a series of self-contained garden rooms. Each garden room offers an abundance of variety in form, foliage and bloom and ensures a continuous display from Spring to Autumn.

The unique restoration project of the 80 yard **double herbaceous border**, to a design by the Chelsea Gold Medallist George Carter, is due to open in Summer 2011. With its stone benches set into the borders, historic varieties of apple trees and the colour coordinated herbaceous and shrub planting, this is a restoration project that will enchant and delight our visitors.

Make your visit complete by visiting our refurbished Garden Tea Room, Gift Shop and Plant Centre and a visit to the historic church close by, with the Sidney family chapel. Estate parkland walks also available.

Fact File

Opening Times: From Saturday 19th February open weekends and then daily from Monday 28th March - Sunday 30th October 2011.

Admission Rates: To Gardens: Adults £7.80, Child (5-16) £5.80, Family Ticket (2+2) £23.00
Cyclists family £19.00 (or £1 off normal admission prices per person).
Entrance to House small additional charge.

Groups Rates: Freeflow (non guided) House & Gardens Adults £7.50, Children £4.50.
Garden or House tours for groups (15+) includes entrance to house & grounds.
House Tours Adults £9.50, Children £5.00. Garden Tours Adults £9.50, Children £5.00.
Combined House & Garden tours: Adults £15.00, Children £9.00
Head Gardener's Tours – additional £65, subject to his availability.
Joint tickets to visit other local attractions available. Contact us for further details.

Facilities: Gift Shop, Garden Tea Room & Garden History Exhibition in Garden Tower.

Disabled Access: Garden Yes, House DVD of state rooms in Baron's Hall
Toilet and parking for disabled on site, wheelchairs on loan, booking necessary.

Tours/Events: Special joint entrance with other nearby attractions. Penshurst cream tea offer and high tea for groups if pre-booked. Events programme.

Coach Parking: Yes.

Length of Visit: 2 - 3 hours

Booking Contact: Head of Visitor Services. Penshurst Place, Penshurst, Nr Tonbridge, Kent TN11 8DG
Telephone: 01892 870307 Fax: 01892 870866

Email: groups@penshurstplace.com **Website:** www.penshurstplace.com

Location: M25 junction 5, follow A21 to Hastings. Exit at Hildenborough then follow brown tourists signs.

Please quote this guide when making a booking

The Secret Gardens are 3.5 acres of stunning Lutyens and Jekyll designed grounds surrounding the The Salutation, a Lutyens manor house in the heart of Sandwich, East Kent. Neglected for 25 years, an extensive restoration and re-planting programme has now returned the Gardens to their former glory.

Some original features have been revived whilst contemporary and traditional planting styles mix harmoniously to create a garden that has evolved and yet still captures the spirit of its heritage. The Gardens include a Tropical and Spring Border, Vegetable, Kitchen, White and Yellow Gardens which create a many "roomed" effect and provide something new to look at around every hedge.

After a stroll in the Gardens visit the Tea Rooms for a reviving cup of tea and a slice of homemade cake, indulge in a cream tea or linger longer for a spot of lunch and a glass of wine.

Fact File

Opening Times:	4th Jan – 31st March, 10-4pm. 1st April - 30th Sept, 10-5pm. 1st Oct – 24th Dec, 10-4pm
Admission Rates:	Adults £6.50, Senior Citizens £6.00, Children (6-16) £3.00, Under 6 FREE, Family £16.00 (2 adults and up to 3 children). Season £25.00, Golden (1+1) £38.00.
Group Rates:	Minimum group size 10. Prices on application.
Facilities:	Licensed Tea Room with outdoor terrace built specifically for groups, space must be pre-booked. Plant Sales and personal Audio Tours.
Disabled Access:	Yes throughout the gardens and into the Tea Room. Parking and toilet facilities on site.
Tours/Events:	Guided tours available if pre-booked. June - Solstice Garden Tours. August - Candlelit Dusk Tours. Please see website for further details and other events.
Car Parking:	Yes.
Coach Parking:	Available in the public car park adjacent to the gardens.
Length of Visit:	2-3 hours
Booking Contact:	Dominic Parker. Tel. 01304 619 919
Email:	info@the-secretgardens.co.uk
Website:	www.the-secretgardens.co.uk
Location:	In the centre of Sandwich town. Follow signs to Quayside carpark; the entrance to the gardens is located at the top right corner of the car park.

Please quote this guide when making a booking

When Elizabeth (the 5th Duchess) commissioned James Wyatt to build the Castle in 1799 she undertook the design and landscaping of the gardens park and grounds herself. She saw the entire Vale of Belvoir as her garden and was merely framing the views with her valley gardens.

Elizabeth's design and the feel of the individual gardens have many overtures brought back from the Grand Tour of an Italian terraced garden. The gardens facing Belvoir are a natural amphitheatre left by the moraines of two glaciers; she used this to her advantage. She designed and built a series of 'root houses' (summer houses), one of which can be seen today in the Duchess's Garden.

As part of the ongoing restoration, there is a new woodland path that leads down to the Duchess's Gardens. These magical woodland gardens, set in a natural amphitheatre with fresh water springs, are carefully planned to ensure plants bloom all year round.

The Duchess is also working on bringing together collections of specialist plants and roses in different areas of the garden so keen gardeners can come and smell the Best Beale rose and the most exquisite peony and such like.

Fact File

Opening Times	Gardens April – September (please check website or phone for details)
	Castle (please check website or phone for details)
Admission Rates	Gardens Adults £5 Senior Citizens £4 Children £3, RHS Members Free on specified dates (please check website or phone for dates)
	Castle Adults £10 Senior Citizens £9 Children £6
Group Rates	Please phone for details.
Facilities	Gift Shop and Tea Room.
Disabled Access	Partial. One bookable wheelchair available (please phone for details)
Toilets	Yes.
Tours/Events	Yes, see website.
Car Parking	Yes.
Coach Parking	Yes.
Length of Visit	Up to 3 hours.
Booking Contact	Sallyann Jackson, Belvoir Castle, Nr Grantham, Leics NG32 1PE
	Tel: 01476 871 023
Email	sjackson@belvoircastle.com
Website	www.belvoircastle.com
Location	Follow brown tourist signs from A1, A52 and A607

Please quote this guide when making a booking

Set in 300 acres of woodland and pleasure grounds, the Victorian walled garden is a unique experience. The garden has been carefully restored to its late Victorian heyday and grows fruit, flowers and vegetables dating from 1901 or earlier. Trained fruit, vegetable beds and cut flower borders are complemented by a range of glasshouses including a peach case, vinery, display house and fernery.

The huge herbaceous borders in the Secret Garden boast a colourful selection of unusual plants, whilst the Sunken Garden near the Hall is planted in pastel shades. There is also a parterre and rose beds, A 400ft long bog garden has been created in the base of the old ha-ha and a Victorian woodland garden is under development.

Fact File

Opening Times: Park open all year, 9am - dusk.
Walled Garden open 10.30am - 5pm in summer, 10.30am - 4pm in winter.

Admission Rates: Adults £5.10, Senior Citizens (over 60's) £4.60, Child £2.60 (2010 prices).
Season Ticket admits 2 Adults & Children all year for £19.50. (2010 prices) or ticket for two admits two people all year round for £14.50 (2010 prices) under 5's go free.

Group Rates: Minimum group size: 15. Freedom visit: Adults £4.50, Senior Citizens £4.30, Child £2.25.
Visit with tour: Adults £7.15, Senior Citizens £6.45, Child £3.60 (includes admission to all areas).

Facilities: Visitor Centre, Shop, Tea Room, Restaurant, Plant Sales.

Disabled Access: Yes. Toilet & parking on site. Wheelchairs & motorised scooters on free loan, booking necessary.

Tours/Events: Guided tours of walled Garden & Hall available - approx 1 1/2 hours.
Special gardening events throughout the year.

Coach Parking: Yes

Length of Visit: 3 - 4 hours

Booking Contact: Stuart Campbell
Normanby Hall Country Park, Normanby, Scunthorpe, DN15 9HU
Telephone: 01724 720588 Fax: 01724 721248

Email: normanbyhall@northlincs.gov.uk

Website: www.northlincs.gov.uk/normanby

Location: 4 miles north of Scunthorpe off the B1430.

Please quote this guide when making a booking

Chelsea Physic Garden London

London's oldest botanic garden is a beautiful oasis of living history in the heart of the capital, home to a unique collection of medicinal and rare plants. Used as a place to teach people about plants and the environment for more than 300 years, today it exists as a self-supporting charity with two main goals: to help children understand more about the environment, and to conserve a 'living history' of medicinal herbs and plant introductions.

This four-acre walled garden is a haven for rare and tender plants, and also has several glasshouses, the largest fruiting olive tree grown outside in Britain and the oldest rock garden in Europe made from rubble from the tower of London. Particularly successful has been the Fortune Tank Pond, installed more than a hundred years ago by the famous collector of Chinese plants, Robert Fortune.

Fact File

Opening Times: 1st Apr - 31st Oct: Wednesdays - Fridays 12 - 5 p.m., Sundays & Bank Holiday Mondays 12 - 6 p.m. Last entry 30 minutes prior to closing.
Late Openings until 10pm on Wednesdays in July and August with last entry at 8.30 p.m.

Admission Charges: Adults: £8.00, Senior Citizens: £8.00, Children & Students: £5.00

Group Rates: £25 per guide + entrance fee. Minimum Group Size: No minimum
Adults: £8.00, Senior Citizens: £8.00, Children: £5.00

On-Site Facilities: Shop, Plant Sales, Licensed Cafe, Teas

Disabled Access: Yes. Wheelchair loan available - booking required.

Toilets on site: Yes

Car Parking on site: No

Coach Parking: No

Guided Tours: Yes, subject to availability. Booking required for groups of eight or more

Length of Visit: 1 - 2 hours

Special Events: Christmas Fair, Summer Lectures and Winter Openings - check our website for more details.

Booking Contact: Group Visits, Chelsea Physic Garden, 66 Royal Hospital Road, London SW3 4HS
Telephone No. 0207 352 5646 Extension 221 Fax No. 0207 376 3910

Email: enquiries@chelseaphysicgarden.co.uk

Website: www.chelseaphysicgarden.co.uk

Location: No. 170 bus from Victoria or Clapham Junction stations to Flood Street stop. Circle/District line to Sloane Square then 10 mins' walk; 20 mins' walk from Imperial Wharf or Battersea Park stations.

Capel Manor Gardens — Middlesex

A beautiful 30 acre estate, first established in the late 13th century, Capel Manor provides a colourful & scented oasis surrounding a Georgian Manor House & Victorian Stables. With over 60 gardens and borders to explore you'll be inspired by prize winning themed gardens, some you may even recognise as previous Chelsea Flower Show winners, as well as front and back model gardens and historical gardens including the latest additions the Old Manor House Garden (opened by her Majesty the Queen in June 2010) and the Family Friendly Garden (a 2010 Chelsea Flower Show Gold Medal Winner). Come and enjoy the stunning scenery, picnic by the lake or relax in the restaurant and finish with a visit to the gift shop. A full and diverse calendar of events also runs throughout the year including art exhibitions, musical and theatrical events and gardening shows. All this, together with the animal stockyard, exotic room, restaurant and plant sales make Capel Manor Gardens an excellent family day out.

Fact File

Opening Times: Open 10am – 5.30pm (last admission at 4pm). Summer Opening: March to October, open daily. Winter Opening: open weekdays only. Closed Xmas eve to 4th January 2011.

Admission Rates: Adults £5.50, Senior Citizens £4.50, Child £2.50, Family Ticket £13.50 (from April 2009).

Group Rates: Minimum group size: 20
Adults: £5.00. Concessions: £4.00 (Senior citizens, disable, students, UB40 holders).
Children: £2.00 (5s and under go free)

Facilities: Visitor Centre, Shop, Restaurant, Dogs allowed entry on lead.

Disabled Access: Yes. Parking for disabled on site. Wheelchairs on loan, booking necessary.

Tours/Events: Please telephone for details of tours and events programme.

Coach Parking: Yes

Length of Visit: 2 - 3 hours

Booking Contact: Julie Ryan
Capel Manor Gardens, Bullsmoor Lane, Enfield, Middx, EN1 4RQ
Telephone: 08456 122 122 Fax: 01992 717544

Email: cservices@capel.ac.uk

Website: www.capelmanorgardens.co.uk

Location: Near junction 25 of M25

Please quote this guide when making a booking

Myddelton House Gardens Middlesex

The Gardens tell a compelling story about one of Britain's most famous self-taught gardeners, artists and expert botanists Edward Augustus Bowles (E A Bowles). He lived in Myddelton House from 1865 to 1954 and dedicated much of his life to creating an exquisite Garden from uninspired parkland, transforming the Gardens with his love of unusual and exotic plants.

The Gardens boast an impressive range of flora and fauna each season, to stimulate your senses. It's worth looking out for the 108 year old Wisteria which turns a brilliant blue when it flowers, cascading through an ancient yew tree, exotics such as Agave and Aloes in summer and the Osmunda regalis which has been growing in the same spot for almost 100 years.

In 2009, the Gardens were awarded a Heritage Lottery Funded Grant, enabling a two year restoration project. In spring 2011 the gardens will become free to visit, with the addition of the Bowles Tea Room, newly renovated Kitchen Garden and a museum.

London Development Agency

Fact File

Opening Times:	Open every day except Christmas and New Year. October – March 10.00 – 15.00, April to September 09.30 – 16.30 (Times may change, please check before visit).
Admission Rates:	Free admission from 1 April 2011
Facilities:	From 1 April there will be a café, heritage centre and shop.
Disabled Access:	Yes. Toilet and car parking on site (most, but not all, paths accessible). Wheelchair loan available (bookable).
Tours/Events:	Guided tours available plus events throughout the year.
Coach Parking:	Yes.
Length of Visit:	3 hours
Booking Contact:	Head Gardener, Myddleton House, Bulls Cross, Enfield, Middlesex EN2 9HG. Tel: 08456 770 600, fax: 01992 719 937
Email:	info@leevalleypark.org.uk
Website:	www.leevalleypark.org.uk
Location:	The Gardens are located close to J25 of the M25 off the A10 near Enfield. Turkey Street station is within walking distance.

Tony Marshall

There have been gardens at Syon since the 15th century when a Brigettine abbey occupied the site of the present house. Recent archaeological excavations have revealed the remains of the 17th century formal gardens created around the house which were swept away by "Capability" Brown when he landscaped the park for the 1st Duke of Northumberland.

The centrepiece of the gardens is the spectacular Great Conservatory, built by the 3rd Duke in the 1820's by Charles Fowler.

The 40 acres of gardens open to visitors are renowned for their extensive collection of rare trees. Brown's lake is overlooked by a Doric column bearing Flora, Goddess of flowers. The vistas across the Thames-side water meadows, still grazed by cattle, give Syon a unique rural landscape so close to the heart of London.

Fact File

Opening Times: Gardens: Mar – Oct daily (closed Dec 25th and 26th) – 10.30 – 17.00. Nov – Feb, weekends & New Year's Day only: 10.30 – 16.00. Last admission 1 hour before closing.
House open: 16th Mar to 30th Oct 2011 Weds, Thurs, Sundays & Bank Holiday Mondays.

Admission Rates: House & Gardens. Adults: £10.00, Concessions: £8.00, Child: £4.00, Family £22.00
Gardens Only. Adults: £5.00, Concessions: £3.50, Child: £2.50, Family £11.00

Group Rates: Available on request.

Facilities: Garden centre, shops & Refectory cafe.

Disabled Access: Disabled access to the gardens. Limited access to the house. Toilet and car parking on site.

Tours/Events: Guided tours + audio available for the house only.

Length of Visit: 1 hour house, 1 hour gardens.

Booking Contact: Emma Hadleigh-Sparks.
Syon House Gardens & Park, Syon Park, Brentford, Middlesex, TW8 8JF.
Tel: 020 8560 0882, Fax: 020 8568 0936

Email: info:syonpark.co.uk

Website: www.syonpark.co.uk

Location: Location map on website. By rail from Waterloo to Kew Bridge then bus as below or North London line to Gunnersbury then bus 237 or 267 to Brentlea Bus stop. Pedestrian entrance 50 yards. Free car park.
Vehicle entrance Park Road, Isleworth, TW8 8JF
Sat Nav Ref: TW7 6AZ

Please quote this guide when making a booking

The Birmingham Botanical Gardens & Glasshouses   W Midlands

Opened in 1832, the Gardens are a 15-acre 'Oasis of Delight' with over 7000 trees, shrubs and plants – one of the finest collections in the Midlands. The Tropical House, full of rainforest vegetation, includes economic plants and a 24ft lily pond. Palms, tree ferns and orchids are displayed in the Subtropical House. The Mediterranean House features citrus fruits and conservatory plants while the Arid House conveys a desert scene. There is colourful bedding on the Terrace plus Rhododendrons, Rose, Alpine, Herb and Cottage Gardens as well as Historic gardens, Pinetum, the Rock Pool and Woodland Walk. The Gardens also feature a Japanese Garden near which is the home of the stunning National Bonsai Collection.

Other attractions include a Children's Playground and Discovery Garden, the Growing Schools Garden, a four-flight Lawn Aviary, art gallery, gift shop and tea-room. Bands play in the Victorian Bandstand on Sundays throughout the summer and Bank Holidays.

Fact File

Opening times:	Open daily from 9am (10am Sundays)
	Closing: April to September - 7pm, October to March - 5pm (or dusk).
Admission Rates:	Adults £7.50, Senior Citizen £4.75, Child £4.75
Groups Rates:	Minimum group size: 10
	Adults £6.50, Senior Citizen £4.50, Child £4.50
Facilities:	Shop, Tea Room, Plant Sales, Children's Discovery Garden, Sculpture Trail, Aviaries, Organic Garden and many Themed Gardens.
Disabled Access:	Yes. Toilet and parking for disabled on site. Wheelchairs on loan, booking necessary.
Tours/Events:	Tours by appointment. Please telephone for details of Special Events programme.
Coach Parking:	Yes by appointment.
Length of Visit:	2 - 4 hours
Booking Contact:	Tony Cartwright
	The Birmingham Botanical Gardens, Westborne Road, Edgbaston, Birmingham, B15 3TR
	Telephone: 0121 454 1860 Fax: 0121 454 7835
Email:	admin@birminghambotanicalgardens.org.uk
Website:	www.birminghambotanicalgardens.org.uk
Location:	Access from M5 junction 3 and M6. follow the signs for Edgbaston then brown tourist signs to Botanical Gardens.

Most people long for tranquillity, a garden they are happy to be in; such is Gooderstone Water Gardens.

Billy Knights, with no training but great enthusiasm began his garden in 1970, according to his own taste; his likes and dislikes were not dictated by fashion. When he died aged 93 in 1994 he left behind an entrancing 6-acre garden that sits comfortably in the Norfolk countryside. From the natural stream he created ponds and flowing waterways spanned by thirteen bridges. With its additional 8-acre Nature Trail and Kingfisher Hide it's truly a haven for people and wildlife.

Combining native and cultivated plants in informal beds, his daughter Coral is endeavouring to further enhance this atmospheric garden. From well-placed seats visitors can enjoy enchanting vistas and the changing moods of the sky reflected in the clear spring water. And the homemade cakes are delicious!

Fact File

Opening times:	10 a.m. – 5.30 p.m. (dusk in winter) Closed 24th, 25th and 26th June 2011.
Admission Rates:	Adults: £5.00, Senior Citizens: £4.50, Children: £2.00
Group Rates:	Minimum Group Size: 15. Adults: £4.25, Senior Citizens: £4.25, Children: £1.50
Facilities:	Plant Sales, Teas
Disabled Access:	Yes
Toilets on site:	Yes
Car Parking on site:	Yes
Coach Parking:	Yes
Length of Visit:	2 – 3 hours
Special Events:	A wonderful show of astilbe first two weeks July.
Booking Contact:	Gooderstone Water Gardens, c/o Sunny Cottage, Lingwood, NR13 4HG Booking Tel No.01603 712913/07730 551945
Email:	coral@sunnycottage.plus.com
Website:	www.gooderstonewatergardens.co.uk
Location:	In west Norfolk, 6 miles SW of Swaffham between Cockley Cley and Oxburgh Hall (N.T.). Brown signed from Swaffham and Oxborough. Swaffham is on A47.

Please quote this guide when making a booking

Hoveton Hall Gardens

Set in the Norfolk Broads area, the gardens offer an exceptional range of plants, design features, landscape and inspiration throughout the season for garden and plant lovers. In early spring masses of narcissi, including many rare and unusual varieties collected during the 20th century, flower in drifts by the lakes and streams in the woodland areas. From late April to end of May the fragrance of the azaleas and rhododendrons is spectacular on the woodland walks; the lake and Water Garden area has beautiful displays of candelabra primulas and other moisture loving plants. During summer, hydrangeas from deep blue to pale pink and purple flank the sides of the main drive whilst the herbaceous borders and Clematis Walk are at their height of displays.

With lakes, streams and wetland areas meandering through the estate together with a large wood, the gardens are also home to extensive birdlife, both migratory and native species.

Fact File

Opening times: February - Winter Woodland Walks, Sun 13th, Sun 20th, Sun 27th. March - Daffodil Sundays, Sun 20th, Sun 27th. April - Sun 3rd, Sun 10th, 12th - 25th (except Sat 16th & Mon 18th). Wed 27th, Thur 28th & Fri 29th. May - Open every day (except Monday 9th, 16th & 23rd). June - Open every day (except Monadys & Tuesdays). July - Open every day (except Saturdays & Mondays). August - Open every day (except Saturdays & Mondays (except bank holiday Monday). September - Open every day (except Saturdays & Mondays) Last day Sun 18th.

Admission Rates: Adults: £6.50, Children (4 & over): £3.00, Wheelchair users & Carers: £4.50, Family Ticket (2 adults & 2 paying children): £17.00, saving £2 off normal admission. Season Tickets are available - see website for details.

Group Rates: Groups are welcome to visit on any day between 1st April and 30th September. If you want to visit on a day we are normally closed to the public there will be additional charges for admission and the tea room. Groups of 25 plus booking and paying in advance on normal open days - £5.50 each. Groups of 25 plus booking and paying in advance on days we are normally closed - £6.50 each (with an additional one off cost of £30 if the tea room is required). A guide can be provided for any group visit at an additional cost of £30.

Facilities: Plant Sales, Teas, Guided Tours. **Disabled Access:** Partial.

Tours/Events: Yes **Coach Parking:** Yes.

Length of Visit: 2 - 3 hours

Booking Contact: Rachel Buxton, Hoveton Hall Gardens, Norwich, Norfolk NR12 8RJ Telephone: 01603 782558 Mobile: 07900 893017

Email: info@hovetonhallgardens.co.uk **Website:** www.hovetonhallgardens.co.uk

Location: Follow brown and white signs off the A1151 just north of Wroxham

Please quote this guide when making a booking

Set in the beautiful Wensum Valley in North Norfolk and famous for hosting BBC Springwatch, this award winning attraction has something to offer all those who love nature, wildlife and the outdoors.

Enjoy the inspirational Millennium Garden recently redesigned and replanted by the gardens original designer Piet Oudolf, the first of his gardens he has redesigned. Discover the striking laces of *Asitlbe chinensis* var. *Taquetii* 'Purpulanze' which are married perfectly with the spun gold *Deschampsia cespitosa* 'Goldtau'. The Garden builds dramatically to its peak in August, and then settles into a stunning new aspect with thousands of seed heads in autumn. The Wave Garden, opened in 2006, has year-round structure and interest, with *Luzula* dipping under the crests of yew and meandering through the resident trees in this lakeside garden. Thousands of bulbs and flowering fruit trees bring splashes of colour in winter and spring to this wooded lakeside garden. Designed by Julie Toll the garden works with nature using calm and naturalistic planting. Also worth wandering through is our Wildlife Habitat Garden which was opened by wildlife presenter Chris Packham and is packed full of hints and tips on how you can attract wildlife into your outside space.

Fact File

Opening times:	10 a.m. – 4 p.m. (January – March)
	10 a.m. – 5 p.m. (April – December)
Admission Rates:	Please call or visit our website for prices.
Group Rates:	Minimum Group Size: 15.
	Please call or visit our website for prices.
Facilities:	Visitor Centre, Shop, Plant Sales, Restaurant, Teas.
Disabled Access:	Yes. Bookable wheelchair loan available.
Toilets on site:	Yes.
Tours/Events:	Guided tours available. Booking required.
Coach Parking:	Yes.
Car Parking on site:	Yes.
Length of Visit:	4-6 hours.
Booking Contact:	Kirsty Willingham
	Pensthorpe Nature Reserve, Norwich Road, Fakenham, Norfolk NR21 0LN
	Telephone: 01328 851465
	Fax: 01328 855905
Email:	info@pensthorpe.com
Website:	www.pensthorpe.com
Location:	1 mile from Fakenham on the A1067 to Norwich.

Please quote this guide when making a booking

Peter Beales Roses are world leaders in Classic Roses. In glorious full bloom, the inspirational rose gardens of Peter Beales are a must for any enthusiast, with over three acres of RHS Chelsea Flower Show gold medal winning varieties, the National Collection of Rosa species and many interesting and colourful companion plants and shrubs. The garden has many points of interest in its room-like layout including an attractive pond with koi carp, pergolas, arbours and archways. Visitors are free to wander and enjoy the beautiful flowers and sensuous perfumes. There is also an excellent licensed Bistro and Garden Centre on site where you can enjoy a meal and a glass of wine or stock up on gardening essentials, luxury gifts and, of course, lots of roses too. There are hundreds of container roses as well as other plants available during the summer or you can choose to order for winter delivery.

Fact File

Opening Times:	Daily 9 a.m. – 5 p.m. Sundays and Bank Holidays: 10 a.m. – 4 p.m.
Admission Rates:	Adults: Free, Senior Citizens: Free, Children: Free.
Group Rates:	Minimum Group Size: 15. Please contact us for further information.
Facilities:	Garden Centre, Gift Shop, Bistro, Gardens. Marquee available for hire.
Disabled Access:	Yes. Bookable wheelchair loan available.
Toilets on site:	Yes.
Tours/Events:	Guided tours available. Booking required.
	Pruning and Planting in the Peter Beales Rose Gardens. A full day of instruction with lunch included to help you get the most from your roses, please enquire.
Coach Parking:	Yes.
Car Parking on site:	Yes.
Length of Visit:	2 hours.
Booking Contact:	Peter Beales Roses, London Road, Attleborough, Norfolk NR17 1AY
	Telephone: 0845 481 0277 Fax: 01953 456845
Email:	events@peterbealesroses.com
Website:	www.peterbealesroses.com
Location:	Approaching from the south – leave the A11 at the Breckland Lodge roundabout. The nursery is approximately 1/2 mile north on the old London Road. Approaching from Norwich, bypass Attleborough and turn left at the roundabout.

Please quote this guide when making a booking

A visit to Sandringham's sixty-acre gardens is a delight at any time of year. Woodland walks, lakes and streams are planted to provide year-round colour and interest; sheets of spring - flowering bulbs, avenues of rhododendrons and azaleas, beds of lavender and roses, dazzling autumn colour - there is always something to see. Other highlights include the formal North Garden, Queen Alexandra's summerhouse beside its own cascading stream, sixteen species of oak and many commemorative trees. Guided garden walks offered regularly.

Open Easter to mid-July and early August to end October, 10.30am to 5pm daily (4pm in October).

Fact File

Opening times:	Easter - mid July and early August - end October
Admission Rates:	Adults £7.50, Senior Citizen £6.50, Child £4.00.
Groups Rates:	Minimum group size: 20, Group discounts available.
Facilities:	Visitor Centre, Gift Shop, Plant Sales, Teas, Restaurant, Sandringham Museum (inc in ticket) Sandringham House (Extra Charge).
Disabled Access:	Yes. Toilet and parking for disabled on site, Wheelchairs on loan.
Tours/Events:	Guided garden walks offered regularly.
Coach Parking:	Yes
Length of Visit:	2 hours. (for Garden only, longer for House and Museum).
Booking Contact:	Mrs N Colman Sandringham, Norfolk. PE35 6EN. Tel: 01485 545400 Fax: 01485 541571
Email:	visits@sandringhamestate.co.uk
Website:	www.sandringhamestate.co.uk
Location:	8 miles northeast of Kings Lynn on A149.

Please quote this guide when making a booking

The Park is listed Grade One in the Register of Parks and Gardens of Special Historic Interest and originates from the 18th Century when Ralph, first Duke of Montagu created an ornamental and intricate landscape, inspired by the ones he had seen at Versailles whilst serving there as English Ambassador to Louis XIV. The River Ise was canalised and lakes, waterways, fountains, ornamental plantings and statuary were added by him and his son John, the Second Duke of Montagu. Avenues of trees created a network of rides stretching out for over seventy miles.

The benign neglect into which the House fell for the remainder of the 18th and 19th centuries was equally beneficial for the landscape. The bones survived, albeit hidden and now the landscape is being restored, inspired by the original plans of 1746. Waterways are being cleared and realigned to the original scheme, whilst many features and avenues are being re-created.

The Orpheus project (pictured left) was commissioned by the 10th Duke of Buccleuch who wished to create a new feature, the first for nearly 300 years, on the empty space opposite the mount. The space is intended for quiet contemplation and music, whilst echoing existing features of the park. An inverted grass pyramid descends, ensuring that the new design is invisible until one draws near.

Fact File

Opening Times:	(2009) Grounds opening May 1st - July 31st, every day except Saturday, August 1st - September 1st every day, noon - 5pm.
Admission Rates:	(2010) Adults £6.00, Children (5-16 years old) £2.00, Family Ticket £14.00 (2+2).
Group Rates:	Please enquire.
Facilities:	Shop, Plant Sales, Toilets.
Disabled Access:	Yes. No charge for wheelchair borne visitors.
Coach Parking:	Yes.
Booking Contact:	Charles Lister, House Manager The Living Landscape Trust Boughton House Kettering Northamptonshire NN14 1BJ Booking Tel Number. 01563 515731 Booking Fax Number. 01536 417255
Email:	llt@boughtonhouse.org.uk
Website:	www.boughtonhouse.org.uk
Location:	Boughton House is situated off the A43, 3 miles north of Kettering and the A14, through the village of Geddingdon.

Castle Ashby House is the ancestral home of the 7th Marquess of Northampton. The house is set amidst a 10,000 acre working estate with an extensive 25 acres of gardens which are open to the public 365 days a year.

Castle Ashby Gardens are a mixture of many different styles including a beautiful butterfly garden, picturesque rainbow border, colourful fuschia house, large arboretum including a nature trail and the formal Italian gardens.

A children's farmyard with a wide selection of rare breed animals can also be found within the gardens and new attractions now also include a tea room and gift shop.

Fact File

Opening Times: 10am – 5;30 pm 1st April to 30th September
10am - 4;30 pm 1st October to 31st March
Admission Rates: Adults: £5.00, OAP/ children over 10 £4.50, Children under 10 free.
Group Rates: All groups welcome - Discount for groups of 25 people or more.
Facilities: Shop, plant sales, restaurant/teas, toilets.
Disabled Access: Yes.
Car Parking on site: Yes
Coach Parking: Yes
Tours/Events: Guided tours available. Booking required.
Length of Visit: 2 – 3 hours.
Special Events: TBC
Booking Contact: Mark Brooks - Head Gardener, Peter Cox - Assistant Head Gardener
Castle Ashby Gardens, Castle Ashby
Northampton NN7 1LQ
Booking Telephone No. 01604 695200 Booking Fax No. 01604 696187
Email: markbrooks@castleashby.co.uk
Website: www.castleashbygardens.co.uk
Location: Castle Ashby is situated off the A428 between Northampton and Bedford, and is also accessible from the A45.

Please quote this guide when making a booking

Coton Manor lies in peaceful Northamptonshire countryside providing an ideal setting for the ten-acre garden.
Originally laid out in the 1920s by the grandparents of the current owner, it comprises a number of smaller gardens, providing variety and interest throughout the season.
The 17th century manor house acts as a central focus for the garden, with the walls supporting unusual climbing roses, clematis and shrubs, while the surrounding York stone terraces are populated by numerous pots and containers overflowing with pelargoniums, verbenas, heliotropes, salvias and agapanthus.

The rest of the garden slopes down from the house and is landscaped on different levels, lending a natural informality. Old yew and holly hedges complement the many luxuriant borders packed with unusual plants (mostly available in the specialist nursery) and displaying inspirational colour schemes throughout the season.
Water is abundant with natural flowing streams, ponds and fountains everywhere.
Beyond the confines of the garden there is a magnificent bluebell wood (early May) and established wildflower meadow (mid-June to mid-July).

Fact File

Opening times:	Friday 1st April – Saturday 1st October 2010 – Tuesday to Saturday and Bank Holiday weekends (also Sundays in April and May): 12 noon – 5.30 p.m.
Admission Rates:	Adults £6.00, Senior Citizens £5.50, Child £2.00.
Group Rates:	Adults £5.00
Facilities:	Restaurant available for group bookings. Cafe serving light lunches and teas, Extensive nursery with many unusual plants mostly grown from the garden. Shop.
Disabled Access:	Yes (difficult in places) Toilet and parking for disabled on site.
Tours/Events:	Tours by appointment (Wednesdays), Hellebore weekends (Mid Feb), Bluebell Wood (late April/early May), Roses (late June).
Coach Parking:	Yes.
Length of Visit:	2 - 2 ½ hours
Booking Contact:	Sarah Ball, Coton Manor Garden, Nr Guilsborough, Northampton NN6 8RQ. Telephone: 01604 740219 Fax: 01604 740838
Email:	pasleytyler@cotonmanor.co.uk
Website:	www.cotonmanor.co.uk
Location:	9 miles NW of Northampton, between A5199 (formerly A50) and A428.

Please quote this guide when making a booking

Cottesbrooke's award winning gardens are made up of a series of individually planted rooms which open up before you and are packed with many unusual plants to add interest and variety. There are many unusual trees in addition to the 300 year old Cedar of Lebanon which towers above the magnificent 65 metre long double herbaceous borders. There is also the wonderful recently designed (Spring 2010) Statue walk border, pools and lily ponds, secret gardens and on the south front the formal parterre frames the amazing vista towards the famous 7th century church at Brixworth. In contrast to the formal gardens that surround the Hall the magical Wild Garden is a short walk across the park and is planted along the course of a stream. Here there are small cascades and arched bridges, wonderful Acers and other specimen trees, rhododendrons, bamboos and gunneras. The gardens are exquisitely peaceful with wildlife aplenty and they offer interest all season long.

A number of distinguished designers have been involved with the gardens at Cottesbrooke including Robert Weir Schultz, Sir Geoffrey Jellicoe, Dame Sylvia Crowe and more recently James Alexander Sinclair and Arné Maynard. Group garden tours with the Head Gardener are available.

Fact File

Opening Times: May 2nd to the end of September. May & June: Wed & Thurs 2pm - 5.30pm, July, Aug & Sept: Thurs 2pm - 5.30pm, Plus Bank Hol Mondays (May-Sept) 2pm - 5.30pm Closed week beginning 20th June 2011 in preparation for Plant Finders Fair.

Admission Rates: House & Gardens: Adults £8.00, Child £3.50. (5 - 14yrs), Concession £6.50 Gardens only: Adults £5.50, Child £2.50 (5 - 14yrs), Concession £4.50

Group Rates: Group and private visit rates on application.

Facilities: Tearoom, Free car park.

Disabled Access: Yes (Gardens only), Toilet and parking for disabled on site. (Please contact administrator regarding disabled access)

Tours/Events: Guided tour of the house (45 mins), Garden tours by arrangement, groups welcome - please pre book. The Cottesbrooke Hall Plant Finders Fair - 24th, 25th and 26th June 2011. See website for more event details.

Coach Parking: Yes.

Length of Visit: 2-2½ hours (Garden) 45 mins (House).

Booking Contact: Via the Administrator on 01604 505 808 or Fax on 01604 505 619 or email enquiries@cottesbrooke.co.uk

Email: enquiries@cottesbrooke.co.uk

Website: www.cottesbrookehall.co.uk

Location: Cottesbrooke is situated 10 miles north of Northampton off the A5199. Easily accessible from the A14 (junction 1 - A5199) and M1/M6.

Please quote this guide when making a booking

Deene Park has been home to the Brudenell family since 1514 and was the seat of the 7th Earl of Cardigan who led the Charge of the Light Brigade in 1854. The largely Tudor house with important Georgian additions is surrounded by historic gardens set in beautiful parkland views.

The gardens are the lifetime work of Mr. Edmund and the Hon. Mrs. Brudenell; comprising a David Hicks parterre with topiary teapots, long mixed borders, 'four seasons' garden with a spectacular planted font and circular hornbeam hedge, stone summerhouse, lakes and wild gardens.

In winter visitors can enjoy swathes of snowdrops, winter flowering shrubs, hellebores and topiary. The seasons progress through drifts of daffodils, hyacinths and wild tulips; with roses, philadelphus, and summer annuals carrying through to the bold autumnal colour of the trees and shrubs.

Fact File

Opening Times:	House & Gardens: Easter Sunday & Monday, Sundays and Bank Holiday Mondays from May to end August, Wednesdays in May, September and 1st June, 2-5 p.m. Last admission 4 p.m. Open for groups at other times by prior arrangement.
Admission Rates:	Adults: House & Gardens: £8.00, Gardens Only £5.50, Senior Citizens: House & Gardens £7.00, Gardens Only £5.50, Children: House & Gardens £4.00, Gardens Only £2.50
Group Rates:	For private visits, pre-booked, Access to Gardens Only £4.50 (minimum £90), House & Gardens: £7.00 (minimum £140). Additional charges at weekends and Bank Holidays apply. Garden tour prices on request.
Facilities:	Shop & Tearoom. Light lunches, suppers and cream teas available, made by the family cook by prior arrangement for group visits. Toilets on-site.
Tours:	House & Garden tours available for groups by prior arrangement.
Events:	'Snowdrop Sundays' Sundays 13 and 20 February 2011 11 am – 4 pm, 'Daffodil Day' Sunday 27 March 11 am – 4 pm.
Disabled Access:	Partial. Disabled Parking on Site.
Car/Coach Parking:	Yes.
Length of Visit:	1-2 hours (excluding house)
Booking Contact:	The Administrator, Deene Park, Nr. Corby, Northamptonshire, NN17 3EW Telephone: 01780 450278 Fax: 01780 450282
Email:	admin@deenepark.com
Website:	www.deenepark.com
Location:	Off A43 between Corby and Stamford

Please quote this guide when making a booking

The award-winning Formal Gardens of Blenheim Palace.

On passing through the triumphal arch at Woodstock gate entrance to Blenheim Palace, it is clear to see why Lord Randolph Churchill proclaimed 'This is the finest view in England'.

The Park was landscaped in the 1760's by 'Capability' Brown, and is hailed as one of his greatest achievements. It is one of the main reasons that the Palace and Park was created a World Heritage site in 1987. The 2,100 acres of sweeping parkland and 100 acres of Formal Gardens provide an awe-inspiring setting for Britain's Greatest Palace.

The stunning Formal Gardens have so much to offer, whether for a group or individuals. An Audio Garden Tour is available throughout the season, with commentary from the Palace experts offering visitors the opportunity to take in the wonders of the gardens at their own pace. From the ornate fountains in the Water Terraces and Lakeside Walks to the elegant Rose Garden and recently restored Secret Garden, there is something for anyone with a love of gardens.

Fact File

Opening Times:	Opening Dates: Saturday 12 February to Sunday 16 December 2011 Saturday 12 February to Sunday 30 October 2011 open daily Wednesday 2 November to Sunday 16 December 2011 open Wed to Sunday.
Opening Times:	Palace & Gardens open daily from 10.30am to 5.30pm (last admission 4.45pm) with areas to be vacated by 6pm Park opens daily from 9am to 4.45pm (last admission) except Christmas Day – all areas to be vacated by 6.30pm latest.
Admission Rates:	Palace, Park & Gardens: Adult £19.00; Concessions £15.00; Child £10.50; Family £50.00 Park & Gardens: Adult £11.00; Concessions £8.00; Child £5.50; Family £28.00
Group Rates:	Palace, Park & Gardens Ticket: Adult £12.70; Concessions £11.00; Child £6.90
Facilities:	Shop, Restaurants, Hampers, Afternoon Teas, Sunday Lunches
Disabled Access:	Yes, toilet on site. Buggies, wheelchairs and mobility scooters available.
Coach Parking:	Yes
Length of Visit:	at least 2 hours
Booking Contact:	Cathy Tuckey, Blenheim Palace, Woodstock, Oxfordshire OX20 1PP Telephone: 01993 811091 Freephone: 0800849 6500 (24hr recorded message) Fax: 01993 810570
Email:	operations@blenheimpalace.com
Website:	www.blenheimpalace.com
Location:	situated in Woodstock eight miles north west of Oxford on A44

Please quote this guide when making a booking

Buscot Park Oxfordshire

Buscot Park was laid out in the late eighteenth century in the English Landscape style to provide a naturalistic setting for the Palladian style house built between 1780 and 1783.

The famous water garden was added in 1904 by Alexander Henderson, later the first Lord Faringdon, who commissioned the architect and garden designer Harold Peto to create a link between the eighteenth century house and the great lake. Peto was the leading exponent of formal Italianate garden design of his day and this water garden is widely regarded as one of his finest works. It consists essentially of a series of stairways, formal lawns, pools and basins interlinked by a descending canal complete with rills, miniature cascades and a bridge all flanked by box hedges sheltering statuary and stone seats.

The present Lord Faringdon continues to enhance the grounds and has transformed the former eighteenth-century kitchen garden into a beautifully structured ornamental garden.

'I consider Buscot Park to be one of England's most unsung country estates' - Tony Russell, Country Gardener Magazine.

Photo of Peto Water Garden by David Dixon

Fact File

Opening Times:	1st April – 30th September
	House, Grounds and Tearoom*: Wed-Fri, 2-6pm (last entry to House 5pm).
	Also open Good Friday, Bank Holiday Mondays and the following weekends:
	9th/10th, 23rd/24th, 30th April: 1st, 14th/15th, 28th/29th May; 11th/12th, 25th/26th June;
	9th/10th, 23rd/24th July; 13th/14th, 27th/28th, August; 10th/11th, 24th/25th September.
	(*Tearoom open 2.30-5.30pm)
	Grounds only: Mon – Tue, 2-6pm
Admission Rates:	Adults: £8.00 (House & Gardens), £5.00 (Gardens only)
	Children (aged 5-16): £4.00 (House and Gardens), £2.50 (Gardens only)
Facilities:	Picnic Area, Homemade Teas, Occasional plant sales.
Disabled Access:	Partial. Adapted Lavatory. Ramps to tearoom, marquee and garden. Two single seater powered mobility vehicles for use in the grounds can be booked in advance.
Coach Parking:	Up to two coaches. Groups **must** book in advance.
Length of Visit:	3 hours
Booking Contact:	Estate Office, Buscot Park, Faringdon, Oxfordshire, SN7 8BU.
	Telephone: 01367 240786 Fax: 01367 241794
Email:	estbuscot@aol.com
Website:	www.buscotpark.com
Information Line:	01367 240932
Location:	Buscot Park is situated on the south side of the A417 between Lechlade and Faringdon

Please quote this guide when making a booking

Cotswold Wildlife Park & Gardens   Oxfordshire

Enjoy a rich diversity of plants and animals from around the globe in a delightful rural setting, as one of the countries foremost exotic gardens plays host to one of the leading animal collections. Over 250 species of animals and several thousand types of plants co-exist throughout our picturesque 150 acres extending around the Regency Gothic manor house.

Towering Bananas, Bamboo, Tree ferns and Palms form the backbone of our celebrated 'Exotic' plantings. During summer and autumn an extensive range of tender foliage and flowering plants enhance the scene, including the Giant Victoria Water lily in the open air. Cactus and succulents inhabit the arid beds around the meerkats; sloths, giant pigeons, tropical birds and Fruit Bats reside in the richly planted Tropical House. Extensive swaths of grasses form a savannah-esk background to rhinos, zebras and giraffes. Visiting is particularly recommended in September when the planting reaches its dramatic climax.

Fact File

Opening Times:	Everyday (except Christmas Day). 10am. (last admission 3.30pm October - February).
Admission Rates:	Adults £12.50, Children and over 65s £8.50.
Group Rates:	Minimum group size: 20 Adults £9.50, Children £6.50 Over 65s £7.00.
Facilities:	Shop, Teas, Restaurant. (Restaurant available for booked lunches and teas, waitress service in Orangery).
Disabled Access:	Yes. Parking for disabled on site. Wheelchairs on loan, booking necessary.
Tours/Events:	Gardens Special for inclusive charge, talk by Head Gardener or his Deputy in the Drawing room of the Manor House and Cotswold Cream Teas in the Orangery.
Coach Parking:	Yes
Length of Visit:	2 ½ - 3 hours
Booking Contact:	General Office. Cotswold Wildlife Park, Burford, Oxfordshire, OX18 4JP Telephone: 01993 823006 Fax: 01993 823807
Email:	feedback@cotswoldwildlifepark.co.uk
Website:	www.cotswoldwildlifepark.co.uk
Location:	On A361 2.5 miles south of A40 at Burford.

Please quote this guide when making a booking

ROUSHAM and its landscape garden should be a place of pilgrimage for students of the work of William Kent (1685 - 1748).

Rousham represents the first phase of English landscape design and remains almost as Kent left it, one of the few gardens of this date to have escaped alteration, with many features which delighted eighteenth century visitors to Rousham still in situ.

The house, built in 1635 by Sir Robert Dormer, is still in the ownership of the same family. Kent added the wings and the stable block. Don't miss the walled garden with their herbaceous borders, small parterre, pigeon house and espalier trees. A fine herd of rare Long-Horn cattle are to be seen in the park.

Rousham is uncommercial and unspoilt with no tea room and no shop. Bring a picnic, wear comfortable shoes and its yours for the day.

Fact File

Opening times:	Every Day All Year
Admission Rates:	Adults £5.00, Senior Citizen £5.00, No Children under 15.
Groups Rates:	None
Facilities:	None
Disabled Access:	Partial, parking for disabled on site.
Tours/Events:	None
Coach Parking:	Yes
Length of Visit:	1 - 2 hours.
Booking Contact:	C Cottrell - Dormer
	Rousham, Nr Steeple Aston, Bicester, Oxon, OX25 4QX.
	Tel: 01869 347110 Fax: 01869 347110
Email:	ccd@rousham.org
Website:	www.rousham.org
Location:	South of B4030, East of A4260.

Situated in a beautiful Chiltern Valley, the walled garden rises up behind the ancient house built and lived in by the Stonor family since the twelfth century. The garden today features swathes of daffodils in April. A field of Narcissi "Pheasant Eye" can be seen through iron gates at the top of the garden, while irises bloom inside the walls in May. Old fashioned roses, peonies and lavenders bloom on the seventeenth century terraces in June, flanked by ancient yew trees and clipped box hedges by the lily ponds. Climbing the terrace stages one finds a long mixed border, ending with a Japanese garden house built by the 5th Lord Camoys after his visit to Kyoto in 1906. The jasmine and rose bower offers spectacular views of the house and deer park. This area was the old kitchen garden now converted by Lady Camoys in the 1980's into a pleasure garden. It is divided into six plots as shown in the seventeenth century painting of the house, which can be seen in the drawing room. Irish yews box hedging and old fruit trees delineate the design.

Fact File

Opening times: Open in 2011 on Sundays (Easter to mid September inclusive), Bank Holiday Mondays and Wednesdays (July and August only)

Admission Rates: House and Gardens: Adult: £8.00, first child (5-16) £4.00, additional children, under 5's free
Gardens only: Adult £4.00, first child (5-16) £2.00, additional children, under 5's free.

Group Rates: Minimum Group Size: 20 A private guided tour is available at £9.00 per person on Tuesday to Thursday, April to September by prior arrangement.

Facilities: House, Chapel, Gardens, Shop, Old Hall Tea Room

Disabled Access: Unsuitable for physically disabled.

Tours: The house, tea room and shop open at 2.00pm - last entry 4.30pm.
Gardens are open on each of the above days between 1.00pm and 5.30pm.

Events: VW Rally (Sunday 5th June 2011),
Chilterns Craft Fair (Friday 26th August - Monday 29th August)

Coach Parking: Yes.

Length of Visit: 1 – 4.5 hours.

Booking Contact: Administrator, Stonor Park, Henley-on-Thames, Oxon RG9 6HF
Tel: 01491 638587 Fax: 01491 639348

Email: administrator@stonor.com

Website: www.stonor.com

Location: Five miles north of Henley-on-Thames, on the B480
Henley-on-Thames – Watlington Road.

Waterperry gardens are steeped in history, with the famous, purely herbaceous border dating back to the 1930's when Beatrix Havergal established her Ladies Horticultural School. Running more than 200 feet along the length of the old kitchen garden wall, the south facing border provides interest from early May to late September, using early, mid-season and late-flowering herbaceous plants and climbers.

New design elements have been incorporated into the 8 acre gardens over the years, including the colour border, showing how to use flowers, stems, autumn foliage and fruit in design. A formal knot garden reflects planting through the ages from Tudor to modern times and there's also a herb border and spectacular white and lavender wisteria arch. The Mary Rose Gardens show how roses can be used in design and there's a waterlily canal, herbaceous nursery stock beds from which all our cuttings are taken for the plants sold in the walled garden plant centre; island beds designed by nurseryman Alan Bloom; an alpine garden and riverside walk.

As well as an art gallery, small rural life museum and teashop, the garden shop sells a full range of garden sundries, gifts and books. Waterperry is an oasis of calm and beauty within easy reach of Oxford.

Fact File

Opening times:	February 12th to October 31st 2011 10am to 5.30pm. November 2011 to February 2012 10am to 5pm. Waterperry Gardens is closed between Christmas and New Year and during Art in Action, July 21st to 24th 2011.
Admission Rates:	Jan 1st to Feb 11th 2011. Adults & concessions £4.20. Children aged 16 and under free. Feb 12th to Oct 31st. Adults £6.10. Concessions £4.70. Children aged 16 & under free. November & December 2011. Adults & concessions £4.30. Children aged 16 & under free.
Group Rates:	Jan 1st to February 11th 2011. £4.20 for groups of 20 or more booked in advance. Feb 12th to Oct 31st 2011. £4.70 for groups of 20 or more booked in advance. Nov and Dec 2011. £4.20 for groups of 20 or more booked in advance.
Facilities:	Garden shop, Plant centre, Teas, Restaurant, Gallery, Museum
Disabled Access:	Yes. Toilet and parking for disabled on site. Wheelchairs on loan.
Tours/Events:	Tours can be arranged. Waterperry has a full programme of annual events from those with a horticultural theme to outdoor concerts and theatre. There's also a full programme of gardening, arts and crafts classes. Please visit our website www.waterperrygardens.co.uk for more information.
Coach Parking:	Yes. Coach drivers also receive a meal voucher on booking.
Length of Visit:	Approximately 3 – 4 hours.
Booking Contact:	Main Office, Waterperry Gardens, Waterperry, Near Wheatley, Oxfordshire OX33 1JZ. Tel 01844 339254. Fax 01844 339883.
Email:	office@waterperrygardens.co.uk
Website:	www.waterperrygardens.co.uk
Location:	7 miles east of Oxford – junction 8 M40 from London. Follow brown signs. Junction 8a M40 from Birmingham.

Please quote this guide when making a booking

The gardens at Hodnet were started in 1922 when there was only a marshy hollow in front of the house. This was excavated, dams built and a chain of seven lakes and pools was created, all planted out with rare trees and shrubs. Rhododendrons and camellias thrive in the acid soil; iris and other bog plants enjoy this fairly high rainfall area and their position around the pools.

April is the perfect time to come and admire the camellias, crocuses and daffodils, not forgetting the magnificent Magnolia Walk. May and June showcases rhododendrons, lilacs, azaleas and bluebell woods. High summer is brimming with peonies, hydrangeas, roses and many other flowering shrubs, the colours lasting right through September. With 63 acres to explore there is something for everyone here.

The half-timbered restaurant serves lunches and teas amongst a unique collection of big game trophies.

Fact File

Opening Times:	12 noon - 5pm
	April: 10th, 17th 24th & 25th (Easter)
	May: 1st & 2nd (BH), 8th, 15th, 22nd, 29th & 30th (BH)
	June: 5th (Plant Hunters Fair) 12th & 19th (NGS)
	July: 3rd, 17th & 27th (Weds)
	August: 7th, 14th, 17th (Weds), 28th & 29th (BH)
	September: 11th & 25th
Admission Rates:	Adults: £5.00, Children: £2.50, no concessions.
Group Rates:	Minimum Group Size: 20. Adults: £5.00, Children: £2.50.
Facilities:	Restaurant - lunches and teas.
Disabled Access:	Yes, partial.
Toilet On Site:	Yes.
Tours:	Yes for groups. Booking required.
Events:	See website.
Coach Parking:	Yes.
Car Parking:	Yes.
Length of Visit:	1 hour minimum.
Booking Contact:	The Secretary, Hodnet Hall, Hodnet, Market Drayton, TF9 3NN
	Telephone No. 01630 685786. Fax No. 01630 685853
Email:	secretary@heber-percy.freeserve.co.uk
Website:	www.hodnethallgardens.org

Wollerton Old Hall Garden

Created 25 years ago around a Tudor house (not open), this quality garden has achieved the highest "Good Garden Guide" rating and RHS Partnership status. Designed by the owner, Lesley Jenkins, this outstanding garden combines a strong structure with clever planting combinations using perennials.

The early spring shows of anemones, hellebores and trilliums are followed by tulips, aquilegias and oriental poppies. The summer roses herald the arrival of the delphiniums which in turn give way to the dominance of stately hollyhocks and vibrant phlox. August sees the hot garden ignited which still burns when the asters and euonymus seed capsules arrive in September.

The garden has significant collections of rare perennials, salvias, paniculata phlox and clematis and many of these are available in the Plant Centre. The Tea Room provides excellent lunches, teas and evening meals with all the food being prepared freshly on the premises.

Joint Tickets: These are available for groups to visit Wollerton and the Trentham Estate on the same day for £10 per person.

Photo Clive Nichols

Fact File

Opening Times:	Public days – Good Friday, every Friday, Sunday and Bank Holiday until end of September: 12 noon – 5 p.m.
Admission Rates:	Adults/Senior Citizens: £5.50 per person, Children 4-15 years: £1.
Group Rates:	Garden groups welcome by appointment on Tuesdays and Wednesdays. Minimum 25, Group rate £5.00 per person.
Facilities:	Plant Sales, Lunches, Teas, large car park for cars.
Disabled Access:	Easy wheelchair access for 80% of the garden. The remainder accessible with helper.
Tours/Events:	Guided tours available: topic-specific garden tours with Head Gardener. Lectures by garden personalities. Evening Summer Strolls with candlelit garden and supper.
Coach Parking:	Coaches welcome by appointment. Coach parking available on the lane outside the garden.
Length of Visit:	2 – 4 hours, depending upon level of plant interest.
Booking Contact:	Diana Oakes. Wollerton Old Hall Garden, Wollerton, Market Drayton, TF9 3NA. Telephone: 01630 685760 Fax: 01630 685583
Email:	info@wollertonoldhallgarden.com
Website:	www.wollertonoldhallgarden.com
Location:	The garden is brown-signed off the A53 between the A41 junction and Hodnet.

Please quote this guide when making a booking

The Walled Gardens Of Cannington Somerset

Located in the village of Cannington, the Walled Gardens lie within the grounds of a mediaeval Priory and many of its fine buildings, including the walls of the garden, remain. Having undergone extensive redevelopment, the gardens were officially opened by HRH the Earl of Wessex, Prince Edward in 2009 and have also been accredited as a 'quality assured visitor attraction' by VisitEngland.

The gardens have classic and contemporary features such as: the 'hot' herbaceous border; the blue garden; a sub-tropical walk; and a Victorian style fernery, amongst others. There is also a botanical glasshouse where arid, sub-tropical and tropical plants can be seen and two smaller gardens within the walls (The Bishop's and Australasian Gardens) are areas of real tranquility.

The plant shop offers a great selection of Cannington-grown plants and gardening accessories and the tea rooms provide homemade food and refreshments in a comfortable setting with ample indoor and outdoor seating.

Fact File

Opening Times:	Winter opening, Mon – Fri 10am – 4pm
	Summer opening, daily 10am – 5pm
Admission Rates:	Adults: £3.50, Senior Citizens: £2.50, Children under 18: free
Group Rates:	Minimum Group Size: 15, per person: £6.00 (includes guided tour, tea/coffee and cake)
Facilities:	Shop, plant sales, tea room
Disabled Access:	Yes
Toilet on site:	Yes
Tours/Events:	Yes, booking required for tours.
Coach Parking:	Yes, by prior arrangement.
Car Parking:	Yes
Length of Visit:	Can stay all day.
Booking Contact:	Walled Gardens Manager
	The Walled Gardens of Cannington and Tea Rooms, Church Street, Cannington,
	Nr. Bridgwater, Somerset TA5 2HA
	Telephone: 01278 655042
Email:	walledgardens@bridgwater.ac.uk
Website:	www.canningtonwalledgardens.co.uk
Location:	Cannington, near Bridgwater, Somerset.
	At the village war memorial, turn onto Church Street and
	follow the brown tourism signs.

Please quote this guide when making a booking

At the foot of Glastonbury Tor, the spring waters of this ancient holy well flow in pools and rills through a beautifully landscaped World Peace Garden.

Visitors are welcomed via the pergola, which in summer drips with fragrant fronds of white wisteria, climbing roses and an abundance of hanging baskets. In the lower gardens the waters run into a Vesica Pool fed by a flow-form cascade set in a rockery. On sunny days the waters sparkle with sunlight, and there is seating available to listen and be soothed by the sounds of tumbling water.

With the renewed interest in healing plants, a physic garden with over 100 specimens has been established including arnica, echinacea, mugwort, valerian, evening primrose and sweet Cicely.

The meadow, entered via a living willow arch training apple trees, is wonderful for picnics and affords views of Glastonbury Tor and the Somerset levels. This is a garden of many "rooms", each with different qualities that create a living sanctuary of peace and tranquillity for all to enjoy.

Fact File

Opening Times:	Open 365 days of the year including Christmas Day & Boxing Day. April 1st to 31st Oct - 10.00 am to 5.30 pm, Nov 1st to March 31st - 10.00 am to 4 pm. We request no smoking, alcohol, or mobile phones. Guide and Assistance Dogs are welcome
Admission Rates:	Adults £3.60, Seniors £3.00, Children £1.80. Gift aid admission available. Special Access allows private hire of the gardens outside public hours, Adult £7.00, Child £4.00,
Group Rates:	Group leaders go free. Normal admission as above.
Facilities:	Onsite Shop, Plant Sales from the Garden. Toilets with disabled access.
Disabled Access:	Motorised wheelchair available, please ask.
Tours:	Outside tours welcome - please see Group Rates above.
Events:	Late night openings with candelit gardens. Our events offer refreshments.
Car/Coach Parking:	Limited - for disabled persons only. Parking available 100 yards at Drapers
Length of Visit:	Allow a minimum of an hour, preferably longer.
Booking Contact:	Office, Chalice Well Gardens, Chilkwell St, Glastonbury, Somerset, BA6 8DD Tel. 01458 831154 Fax. 01458 835528
Email:	Email: info@chalicewell.org.uk **Website:** www.chalicewell.org.uk
Location:	The Chalice Well is situated at the foot of Glastonbury Tor, on the A361, towards Shepton Mallet. Between May and September a shuttle bus runs between the town center, (outside the Abbey), Chalice Well and the Tor, so you can park your car in one of the town center car parks if you wish. Chalice Well is 15 minutes walk from the town centre.

Please quote this guide when making a booking

Five miles West of Wellington, hidden in the high-banked lanes of Somerset, lies Cothay, built at the end of the Wars of the Roses in 1485. Virtually unchanged in 500 years, this sleeping beauty sits on the banks of the river Tone within its twelve acres of magical Gardens.

The Gardens, laid out in the 1920's, have been re-designed and replanted within the original structure. Many garden rooms, each a garden in itself, are set off a 200 yard yew walk. In addition there is a bog garden with azaleas and drifts of primuli, a cottage garden, a courtyard garden, river walk and fine trees. A truly romantic plantsman's paradise. Two stars in the Good Garden Guide.

Fact File

Opening Times: First Sunady in April to end September, Tues, Wed, Sun, & BH - 11am with last entry 4pm.
Admission Rates: Prices vary - Please visit our website.
Group Rates: Groups (20+) are welcome every day of the season by appointment. For further information please contact us, or download a booking form from our website. Click on Groups.
Facilities: Plant Sales, Cream Teas, (Groups 20+ catering by arrangement).
Disabled Access: Yes (Garden) Partial (House), Toilet and parking for disabled on site.
Tours: On Sundays (during the season) at **11.45am and 2.45pm groups** from the general public will be guided round the manor, 1 1/4 hours. Otherwise the manor is only open to groups of 20+ by appointment throughout the year.
Events: For Events please visit our website.
Coach Parking: Yes.
Length of Visit: 1 1/2 - 3 1/2 hours
Booking Contact: The Administrator, Cothay Manor, Greenham, Wellington, Somerset, TA21 0JR
Telephone: 01823 672 283
Email: cothaymanor@btinternet.com
Website: www.cothaymanor.co.uk
Location: From junction 26 M5, direction Wellington, take A38 direction Exeter, 3 1/2 miles turn right to Greenham. From junction 27 M5 take A38 direction Wellington, 3 1/2 miles take 2nd turning left to Greenham.

Please quote this guide when making a booking

One of England's best-loved privately-owned gardens created by the late Margery Fish, celebrated plantswoman and gardening writer, between 1938 and 1969. Her talent for combining old-fashioned and contemporary plants in a relaxed and informal manner has created an extraordinary and unusual garden of great charm.

Now Grade-I listed and renowned as the premier example of the English cottage gardening style, it is noted for its many small paths dividing densely planted beds. It remains a true plantsman's garden, having over 85 varieties of rare snowdrop and extensive collections of hellebores and geraniums. New owners intent on improving the garden arrived in 2008 and work is underway on restoring Margery Fish's 'Green Garden', an area overgrown for more than 20 years.

The Margery Fish Plant Nursery stocks an extensive selection of hardy plants including geraniums, with many propagated from plants growing in the garden.

Fact File

Opening Times:	February, May, June & July daily 10a.m. - 5p.m.
	March-April & August-October: Tuesday-Saturday & Bank Holiday Mondays, 10a.m. - 5p.m.
Admission Rates:	Adults: £5.50, Senior Citizens: £5.00, Children under 16 free.
	RHS Members Free in February, March, September & October.
Group Rates:	Minimum Group Size: 10. Adults: £4.80, Senior Citizens: £4.80, Children under 16 free.
	All group visits receive an introductory talk by Head Gardener/owner.
Facilities:	Plant sales, teas. Malthouse Gallery has regular exhibitions. Excellent lunches available at C17 Rose & Crown pub directly opposite the garden.
Disabled Access:	Yes, partial.
Toilet On Site:	Yes, including a toilet for people with disabilities.
Tours/Events:	Yes, booking required. See website for details.
Coach Parking:	Yes.
Car Parking:	Yes.
Length of Visit:	1-2 hours.
Booking Contact:	Mike Werkmeister,
	East Lambrook Manor Gardens, East Lambrook, South Petherton, Somerset TA13 5HH
	Booking Telephone No. 01460 240328
Email:	mike@eastlambrook.com
Website:	www.eastlambrook.com
Location:	Four minutes from A303 South Petherton roundabout which is 3 miles south of A3088 Yeovil roundabout. Follow brown signs.

Please quote this guide when making a booking

Lose yourself in 40 acres of walks, streams and temples, vivid colours, formal terraces, woodland, lakes, cascades and views that take your breath away.

This is Hestercombe: a unique combination of three period gardens. The Georgian landscaped garden was created in the 1750's by Coplestone Warre Bampfylde, whose vision was complemented by the addition of a Victorian terrace and Shrubbery and the stunning Edwardian gardens designed by Sir Edwin Lutyens and Gertrude Jekyll. All once abandoned, now being faithfully restored to their former glory: each garden has its own quality of tranquillity, wonder and inspiration.

Free entry to our fabulous Courtyard Café and excellent shop; conference and business facilities, weddings, parties, year round events.

Fact File

Opening Times:	Open every day 10am - 6pm (last admissions 5pm).
Admission Rates:	Adults £9.50*, Senior Citizen £8.80*, Children £3.60* (5 - 15yrs) under 5's Free. *Includes 10% voluntary donation towards the continuing restoration.
Group Rates:	Groups 20 or more £7.00, Groups 10 or more £7.50. Tour Guide £60.00
Facilities:	Visitor Centre with Courtyard Café, restored 17th Century Watermill, Shop, Plant Sales. Function Rooms.
Disabled Access:	Partial. Toilet & parking for disabled on site. Wheelchairs on loan, booking advisable.
Tours/Events:	A wide range of events including Themed Fairs, Food Markets, Childrens Trails and many other seasonal events. Walks. Garden tours available for groups.
Coach Parking:	Yes
Length of Visit:	Refreshment stop or part to full day out.
Booking Contact:	Hestercombe Gardens, Cheddon Fitzpaine, Taunton, Somerset, TA2 8LG Telephone 01823 413923 Fax: 01823 413747
Email:	groupbookings@hestercombe.com
Website:	www.hestercombe.com
Location:	4 miles from Taunton, Signposted from all main roads with the Tourist Information Daisy symbol.

Please quote this guide when making a booking

Consall Hall Staffordshire

The Consall Hall Landscape Gardens lie on the edge of the beautiful Churnet Valley where four intersecting valleys form an exceptional 70 acre landscape.

Over the last fifty years, William Podmore OBE has developed the gardens to create a series of beautifully composed rural vistas. These have been enhanced by the construction of six lakes, bridges, follies, grottoes and other focal points, set against the enclosing shelter belts planted with swathes of trees and shrubs, to form a colourful background.

The viewing points have been made easily accessible by the construction of four miles of paths at different levels, and the edges screened with trees so that the views are hidden until the vista is revealed on reaching the correct view point, where a seat is provided.

In many cases, the seat is enclosed so the picture is framed to concentrate the attention on the carefully selected composition, and the views can be enjoyed whatever the weather.

Fact File

Opening times: From start of April – October 10am – 5pm
Sundays, Wednesdays, all Bank Holiday Mondays and Good Friday

Admission Rates: Adults £5.50, Children under 10 £1.50, Family - 2 Adults and 3 Children £13.00

Group Rates: 40+ Exclusive access on none public days. Below 40 by appointment.
Good offers for all group bookings

Facilities: Toilets, Gift shop, Tea room/restaurant, plants for sale, Conducted Buggy tours

Disabled Access: Large Disabled Toilet, Parking

Tours Events: Fully conducted buggy tours, Bookings advised

Coach Parking: Yes, excellent coach parking

Length of Visit: At least 4 hours

Booking Contact: Michelle Swann or Justin Ball
Consall Hall Landscape Gardens, Consall, Wetley Rocks, Staffordshire Moorlands, ST9 0HG
Telephone: 01782 551947

Email: consallgardens@yahoo.com

Website: www.consallgardens.co.uk

Location: From the main A52 Stoke – Ashbourne road take the A522
(Wetley Rocks – Cheadle). Follow brown signs 3/4 mile beyond
Consall village, signposted 'No Through Road'

Please quote this guide when making a booking

Set amongst glorious views of the Staffordshire countryside, this beautiful garden, created by local landowner, Colonel Harry Clive, for his wife Dorothy, embraces a variety of landscape features. They include a superb woodland garden etched from a disused gravel quarry, an alpine scree, a fine collection of specimen trees, spectacular summer flower borders and many rare and unusual plants to intrigue and delight.

A host of spring bulbs, quickly followed by a magnificent display of *Rhododendrons* and *Azaleas* start the season off. Meanwhile the summer season brings with it a wonderful set of flowering herbaceous and mixed borders to admire. Finally the summer gives way to a stunning autumn floral foliage and berry spectacle.

A fine tearoom, overlooking the garden, provides a selection of home baking and light lunches.

Fact File

Opening Times:	Saturday 19th March - Sunday 25th September. New for 2011 Special openings out of season, see website for details
Admission Rates:	Adults £6.00, Senior Citizen £5.00, Child Free.
Group Rates:	Minimum group size: 20, Daytime £4.50, Evening £6.50. Group leader/organiser & driver free entry & refreshments.
Facilities:	Teas
Disabled Access:	Yes, Toilet and parking for disabled on site. Wheelchairs on loan, booking necessary.
Toilet On Site:	Yes.
Tours/Events:	Tours may be organised via prior arrangement.
Coach Parking:	Yes.
Car Parking:	Yes.
Length of Visit:	2 hours
Booking Contact:	The Administrator The Dorothy Clive Garden, Willoughbridge, Market Drayton, Shropshire, TF9 4EU Telephone: 01630 647237 Fax: 01630 647237 (Please call prior to faxing)
Email:	info@dorothyclivegarden.co.uk
Website:	www.dorothyclivegarden.co.uk
Location:	On the A51, two miles south from the village of Woore. From the M6 leave at Junction 15, take the A53, then the A51

Please quote this guide when making a booking

Ham House and Garden

Built in 1610, Ham House was owned by Elizabeth Murray from the 1650's until her death in 1698. With her second husband, the Duke of Lauderdale, she spent much of her enthusiasm and money creating the impressive formal gardens, in keeping with the fashionable court of Charles II. Over the years nature encroached on the garden, hiding the 1670's design. In 1975 the National Trust reinstated its appearance by recreating Elizabeth's garden, using drawings, plans and documentary evidence from the time. Today the gardens survive as a rare example of an original 17th century garden layout.

The iconic formal parterre in the Cherry Garden is Ham's most well-known feature, looking spectacular through the seasons. Walk through the shady hornbeam arch to the grandiose Plats, which lead you to the more intimate Wilderness garden, with period planting, and compartments of British native wildflowers. The ornamental walled Kitchen Garden supplies produce to the stunning Orangery cafe sited along one of its sides and adorned with a breath-taking Wisteria.

Fact File

Opening Times:	House: 12 Feb-29 Nov. Garden Shop & Cafe: 1 Jan-11 Feb, 11-4pm, 12 Feb-30 Oct, 11-5pm 31st Oct-18 Dec, 11-4pm. 1 Jan-31 March free garden tours, Thur, Sat, Sun 1-2pm. Special Christmas openings check opening times with property or ask for an events leaflet.
Admission Rates:	House & Garden £10.90 (£9.90) Child £6.05 (£5.50) Family £27.90 (£25.30)
Group Rates:	£8.40 per person, group visits outside normal opening hours £14.70 per person Garden Only: £3.65 (£3.30), Child £2.45 (£2.20), Family £9.75 (£8.85) Reduced rate Jan - 12 Feb. Standard admission prices in brackets. Gift aid admission includes a voluntary donation of at least 10% which will be put towards the restoration and upkeep of this property.
Facilities:	Shop/Plant Sales/Cafe/Discovery Room/Family Garden Trails/Drop Off point for coaches
Disabled Access:	Yes. **Toilets on Site.** Toilet adapted for visitors with disabilities also available.
Car/Coach Parking:	Cars (free, 40 yards, not National Trust) Coaches (30 yards, confirm availability in advance)
Wheelchair Loan:	Yes (3 wheelchairs available), no booking required.
Guided Tours:	Yes
Length of Visit:	Minimum of 45 minutes for the house and 45 minutes for the garden
Special Events:	Regular programme throughout the year, including selection of guided tours, open air theatre, cinema, opera and garden specific events
Booking Contact:	The Property Office, Ham Street, Richmond-upon-Thames, Surrey, TW10 7RS Telephone: 020 8940 1950 Fax: 020 8439 8241
Email:	hamhouse@nationaltrust.org.uk **Website:** www.nationaltrust.org.uk/hamhouse
Location:	On South Bank of River Thames, west of A307, between Richmond and Kingston. Ham Gate exit of Richmond Park, readily accessible from M3, M4, M25

Please quote this guide when making a booking

Part of the magnificent grounds of Loseley Park, the original two and a half acre Walled Garden is largely based on a design by Gertrude Jekyll.

The Walled Garden features five exquisite gardens, each with its own theme and character. The award-winning Rose Garden is planted with over one thousand bushes, mainly old-fashioned varieties. The extensive Herb Garden contains four separate sections devoted to culinary, medicinal, household and ornamental. The Fruit and Flower Garden is designed to provide interest and bold, fiery colour throughout the season. The White Garden, in total contrast, is planted with white, cream and silver plants, with two water features, creating an idyllic and tranquil area. The Organic Vegetable Garden is spectacular with a huge variety and the Wild Flower meadow is an attractive display during the summer months. Other features include the magnificent vine walk, mulberry tree, ancient wisteria and moat which runs almost the entire length of the Walled Garden and is abundant with wildlife and pond plants.

Fact File

Opening times: Gardens open: May - September, Tuesday - Sunday 11am - 5pm.
Loseley House open (guided tours only): May - August, Tues - Thurs & Sun, 1pm - 5pm.
May and August Bank Holidays.

Admission Rates: Gardens only: Adults £4.50, Senior Citizens £4.00, Child £2.25.
House & Gardens: Adults £8.00, Senior Citizen £7.50, Child £4.00.
Friend of Loseley: £25.00 per annum. (Full details on application).

Groups Rates: Minimum group size: 10. Adults £7.00, Child £3.50

Facilities: Courtyard Tea Room & light snacks, Gift shop, Plant Sales.

Disabled Access: Yes. Toilet and parking for disabled on site. Wheelchair on loan.

Tours/Events: House tours and garden tours for groups by arrangement.

Coach Parking: Yes

Length of Visit: 4 hours

Booking Contact: Group Co-Ordinator
Loseley Park, Estate Office, Guildford, Surrey, GU3 1HS
Telephone: 01483 405112   Fax: 01483 302036 General Information: 01483 304440

Email: groups@loseleypark.co.uk

Website: www.loseleypark.co.uk

Location: 3 miles south of Guildford via A3 and B3000.

Please quote this guide when making a booking

Discover 158 acres of magnificent award-winning authentically restored 18th Century Georgian landscape garden with follies, a Serpentine lake and spectacular views across Surrey.

Features include a unique crystal Grotto, romantic Ruined Abbey, the Gothic Temple, a Turkish Tent and the Gothic Tower. Throughout the year from snowdrops to autumn colour; the plantings, National Collection of North American trees and shrubs, walled garden exhibition and Vineyard offer seasonal interest. Entertaining events and talks are held all year.

The licensed tearoom serves morning coffees, light lunches and afternoon teas, and the gift shop offers a range of gifts and books, as well as Painshill wine and honey.

Fact File

Opening Times: Open all year. (Closed Christmas Day and Boxing Day) March - October 10.30am – 6pm or dusk if earlier (last entry 4.30pm) November – February 10.30am – 4pm or dusk if earlier (last entry 3pm). The Grotto has limited opening hours. Opened for groups by appointment.

Admission Rates: Adults: £6.60. Concessions: £5.80. Children (5 – 16): £3.85, under 5's: Free. Carer of Disabled Person: Free. Family Ticket (2A & 4C): £22.00. Dogs on a lead welcome.

Group Rates: Pre-Booked Adult Groups of 10+: £5.80 plus £1.00 per person for a Guided Tour. Free Entry & Refreshments for Group Organiser and Coach Driver.

Facilities: Gift Shop, Licensed Tearoom (Group menu available), Picnic area, Education visits, Classrooms, Meeting room & permanent Marquee for weddings, private & corporate hire.

Disabled Access: Accessible route. Toilet and parking on site. Free of charge pre-booked Wheelchair loan and Buggy tours (Capacity Max. 3) available for registered disabled persons.

Tours/Events: Guided tours for pre-booked Groups. Events throughout year, telephone or visit website for details. Walled garden exhibition and National Plant Collection.

Coach Parking: Yes. Free

Length of Visit: 2 – 4 hours.

Booking Contact: The Bookings Manager, Painshill Landscape Garden, Portsmouth Road, Cobham, Surrey KT11 1JE. Tel: 01932 868113, Fax: 01932 868001

Email: Info@painshill.co.uk

Website: www.painshill.co.uk

Location: Just off M25/J10/A3 to London. Exit A245 towards Cobham. Entrance on Between Streets, 200m East of A245/A307 roundabout. Nearest Station Cobham/Stoke d'Abernon. Bus Route 515/515A.

Please quote this guide when making a booking

Ramster is famous for its stunning collection of rhododendrons and azaleas, which flourish under the mature woodland canopy. Established in the 1900s by Gauntlett Nurseries of Chiddingfold, with influences from the Japanese gardens, it now stretches over twenty acres. April heralds the arrival of many varieties of daffodils, complementing the camellias, the early flowering rhododendrons and the stunning magnolias. The carpets of scented bluebells contrast exquisitely with the fiery display of azaleas and rhododendrons in May and the warmth of June brings forth the Mediterranean grasses, and the subtle pink climbing roses. In the bog garden a mass of colourful primulas cascade down the rill, and stepping-stones weave a path under the leaves of the giant gunnera.
Always peaceful and beautiful the changing colours are reflected in the pond and lake. Wildlife abounds throughout the season, including kingfishers, herons, ducks, geese and moorhens.

Fact File

Opening times:	Garden and Tea House are open 1st April – 19th June 2011: 10.00 a.m. – 5.00 p.m. Ramster Textile Art and Embroidery Exhibition 8th - 21st April 2011.
Admission Rates:	Adults: £5.00, OAP £4.50, Children: Under 16 – free.
Group Rates:	Minimum Groups Size: 10 Group Adults: £4.50, Children: Under 16 – free.
Facilities:	Plant sales, homemade teas, sandwiches and snacks.
Disabled Access:	Yes. Toilet and car parking on site.
Tours/Events:	Guided tours available for groups of over 20, please book.
Coach Parking:	Yes.
Length of Visit:	Between 2-4 hours.
Booking Contact:	Ramster Gardens, Petworth Road, Chiddingfold, Surrey GU8 4SN Telephone: 01428 654167 Fax: 01428 642481
Email:	info@ramsterweddings.co.uk
Website:	www.ramsterweddings.co.uk
Location:	1½ miles south of Chiddingfold on the A283

Please quote this guide when making a booking

The Trustees are delighted to welcome visitors to Titsey Place and Gardens. The House which dates back to the 17th Century is home to four stunning Canaletto paintings, superb collection of porcelain and objets d'arts belonging to the Leveson Gower and Gresham families who have owned this beautiful mansion house in the North Downs. The gardens extend to some 15 acres and are a mix of formal lawns and rose gardens to informal walks around the two lakes. There is a modern Etruscan temple, walled kitchen garden and four miles of woodland walks.
For further information visit www.titsey.org or telephone 01273 715359.

Fact File

Opening Times:	1 p.m. – 5 p.m. Mid-May to End September on Wednesdays and Sundays. Additionally open summer bank holidays. The garden only open on Easter Monday, plus all Saturdays (gardens only) 12th May to 29th September.
Admission Rates:	Adults: £7.00, Senior Citizens: £7.00, Garden only: £4.50.
Group Rates:	Please telephone for details Adults/Senior Citizens/Children: £8.50
Facilities:	Picnic Area and Tea Rooms.
Disabled Access:	Yes, but garden not very easy. Toilet and parking on site.
Tours/Events:	Guided tours of house & garden, 1.30pm, 2.30pm & 3.30pm. Private tours available by arrangement.
Coach Parking:	Yes. By arrangement only.
Length of Visit:	1 hour garden / 1 hour house.
Booking Contact:	Kate Moisson Titsey Place Gardens, Titsey Place, Oxted, Surrey RH8 0JD Telephone: 01273 715356 Fax: 01273 779783
Email:	brighton@struttandparker.com
Website:	www.titsey.org
Location:	From the A25 between Oxted & Westerham turn left onto B629 and at the end of Limpsfield High Street turn left & follow signs to visitors car park.

Please quote this guide when making a booking

Great Dixter House & Gardens East Sussex

Great Dixter House & Gardens   **East Sussex**

Great Dixter was the birthplace and home of gardening writer Christopher Lloyd. Built c1450 it boasts the largest surviving timber-framed hall in the country which was restored and enhanced by Sir Edwin Lutyens.

The magnificent gardens are now the hallmark of Christopher who devoted his lifetime to creating one of the most experimental gardens in the country, including flower meadows, ponds and the famous Long Border and Exotic Garden. Great Dixter Nurseries offer a wide range of rare and interesting plants that can be seen in the fabric of the garden. Head Gardener Fergus Garrett will lead a number of educational Study Days during the year, please see website for details.

Fact File

Opening Times:	1st April – 30th October Tuesday – Sunday and Bank Holiday Mondays House: 2 – 5 p.m., Garden: 11.00 – 5 p.m.
Admission Rates:	Adults House & Garden: £8.70, Children House & Garden: £4.20. Adults Garden Only: £7.20, Children Garden Only: £3.70.
Group Rates:	Min Group Size: 25, Adults: £7.20, Children: £3.20. Annual tickets available.
Facilities:	Shop, Plant sales, Light Refreshments.
Disabled Access:	Limited. Bookable wheelchair loan available.
Toilets on site:	Yes.
Tours/Events:	Guided tours available, booking required. Study Days, (Horticultural Lectures)
Coach Parking:	Yes.
Car Parking on site:	Yes.
Length of Visit:	2 hours.
Booking Contact:	Jude Churchman. Great Dixter House & Gardens, Great Dixter, Northiam, Rye, East Sussex TN31 6PH Telephone: 01797 254042 Fax: 01797 252879
Email:	groupbookings@greatdixter.co.uk
Website:	www.greatdixter.co.uk
Location:	Signposted from the centre of Northiam on the A28.

Please quote this guide when making a booking

Gardens & Grounds of Herstmonceux Castle   East Sussex

Herstmonceux is renowned for its magnificent moated castle, set in beautiful parkland and superb Elizabethan Gardens. Built originally as a country home in the mid 15th century, Herstmonceux Castle embodies the history of medieval England and the romance of renaissance Europe. Set among carefully maintained Elizabethan Gardens and parkland, your experience begins with your first sight of the castle as it breaks into view.

In the grounds you will find the formal gardens including a walled garden dating from before 1570, a herb garden, the Shakespeare Garden, woodland sculptures, the Pyramid, the water lily filled moat and the Georgian style folly.

The Woodland walks will take you to the remains of three hundred year old sweet chestnut avenue, the rhododendron garden from the Lowther/Latham period, the waterfall (dependent on rainfall), and the 39 steps leading you through a woodland glade.

Fact File

Opening Times:	16th April - 30th October, open daily.
Admission Rates:	Adults £6.00, Senior Citizen £4.95, Child £3.00 (5-15yrs).
Group Rates:	Minimum group size: 15
	Adults £4.50, Senior Citizen £4.00, Child/Students £2.00 (5-15yrs).
Facilities:	Visitor Centre, Gift Shop, Tea Room, Nature Trail, Children's Woodland Play Area.
Disabled Access:	Limited. Toilet and parking for disabled on site. 1 Wheelchair on loan. booking advisable.
Tours/Events:	Guided Tours are conducted at an extra charge and subject to availablity.
	Please telephone for confirmation of tours before you visit.
Coach Parking:	Yes
Length of Visit:	2 - 4 hours
Booking Contact:	Caroline Cullip
	Herstmonceux Castle, Hailsham, East Sussex, BN27 1RN
	Telephone: 01323 834457 Fax: 01323 834499
Email:	c_cullip@bisc.queensu.ac.uk
Website:	www.herstmonceux-castle.com
Location:	Located just outside the village of Herstmonceux on the A271, entrance is on Wartling Road.

Legend has it that King John II, who became King of France in 1350, was held hostage in this house for some years. King John's Lodge is a listed Jacobean house surrounded by a garden for all seasons. Snowdrops and hellebores precede spring bulbs, wild orchids, primroses and violets. This exceptionally romantic garden is noted for its roses, especially those cascading over apple trees in the wild garden. The borders around the formal garden are planted with softly-coloured roses and clematis and herbaceous plants. The year ends with carpets of pink and white cyclamen. The five acre garden is surrounded by meadows with fine trees, grazing sheep and panoramic views. There are a number of water features including a lily pond and fountain in the formal garden, a wild pond and a secret pond in the woodland area. A propagation nursery and shop has now opened selling a wide range of unusual perennials and shrubs, statuary and iron work as well as a range of interesting garden equipment and gifts.

Fact File

Opening Times:	April - October: 10am - 5pm (closed Tuesdays) November - March: 10am to 4pm (closed Tuesdays) Closed in January and February.
Admission Rates:	Adults: £4.00, Children (0-16yrs): Free
Group Rates:	Minimum Groups Size: 10 for concession price £3.50
Facilities:	Shop, plant sales, teas, lunch by arrangement, B&B and holiday accommodation
Disabled Access:	Car parking on site and garden access
Coach Parking:	Yes
Length of Visit:	1 hour
Booking Contact:	Jill Cunningham King John's Lodge, Sheepstreet Lane, Etchingham, East Sussex TN19 7AZ Telephone: 01580 819232 Nursery: 01580 819220
Email:	kingjohnslodge@aol.com or kingjohnsnursery@btconnect.com
Website:	www.kingjohnsnursery.co.uk
Location:	2 miles west of Hurst Green. A265 Burwash to Etchingham. Turn left before Etchingham Church into Church Lane which leads into Sheepstreet Lane after 1/2 mile. On the left after 1 mile, the entrance and parking is at King John's Nursery.

Please quote this guide when making a booking

A garden not be missed - Merriments Garden at Hurst Green offers everything for the "Garden Lover's" day out.

Set in 4 acres of gently sloping Weald farmland, this is a garden of richly and imaginatively planted deep curved borders, colour themed and planted in the great tradition of English gardening. These borders use a rich mix of trees, shrubs, perennials, grasses and many unusual annuals which ensure an arresting display of colour, freshness and vitality in the garden right through to its closing in autumn. Also in the garden are two large ponds, dry scree area, bog and wilder areas of garden planted only using plants suited for naturalising and colonising their environment. It delights all who visit.

The extensive Nursery offers a wide choice of unusual and interesting plants for sale many of which can be seen growing in the garden.

Fact File

Opening times:	Easter to 30th September.
Admission Rates:	Adults £5.00, Senior Citizens £5.00, Child £2.00.
Group Rates:	Minimum group size: 15 (£4.50 per Adult)
Facilities:	Gift Shop, Plant Sales, Restaurant, Wild Bird Centre.
Disabled Access:	Yes. Toilet for disabled on site, Wheelchairs on loan booking advisable.
Tours/Events:	None
Coach Parking:	Yes
Length of Visit:	2 - 3 hours
Booking Contact:	Taryn Murrells
	Hawkhurst Road, Hurst Green, East Sussex. TN19 7RA.
	Telephone: 01580 860666 Fax: 01580 860324
Email:	taryn@merriments.co.uk
Website:	www.merriments.co.uk
Location:	15 miles north of Hastings just off the A21 at Hurst Green.

Please quote this guide when making a booking

Pashley Manor Gardens East Sussex

Nicola Stocken Tomkins

'One of the finest gardens in England' award winning Pashley Manor Gardens, former home of the Boleyns, offers a sumptuous blend of romantic landscaping, imaginative plantings and fine old trees, fountains, springs and large ponds with exceptional views over the surrounding countryside.

Whatever month you choose to visit there is something to delight the senses. Through April to May the bluebells carpet the woodland, the magnificent wisteria cascades down the rear of the house and there are thousands of tulips. June is fragrant with roses and lavender while in July the scent of sweet peas and lilies begin to perfume the air. Summer bedding plants continue through into August, then the hot borders come into their own with many late flowering herbaceous perennials.

Pashley prides itself on its delicious homemade food which visitors can enjoy in the Garden Room Café with Terrace. The new gift shop caters for every taste from postcards to traditional hand painted ceramics, and there is an exhibition and sale of sculpture and botanical art.

Special Events include: Tulip Festival; Sculpture in Particular; Rose Weekend; Kitchen Garden Weekend; Lily Time; and the Sussex Guild Craft Show.

Fact File

Opening Times:	2nd April - 29th September, Tuesday, Wednesday, Thursday, Saturday, Bank Holiday Mondays and Special Event Days 11am - 5pm.
Admission Rates:	Adults £8.50, Children £5.00.
Groups Rates:	Minimum group size 15, Adults £8.00. Tulip Festival £9.00 no concessions.
Facilities:	New Gift Shop, Plant Sales, Licensed Café, Light Lunches and Afternoon Teas.
Disabled Access:	Limited. Toilet and parking for disabled on site. Wheelchairs on loan, booking necessary.
Tours/Events:	Pre-booked tours of garden available. Please call for special event details.
Coach Parking:	Yes
Length of Visit:	2 1/2 hours - half day.
Booking Contact:	Pashley Manor Gardens, Ticehurst, East Sussex, TN5 7HE Tel: 01580 200888 Fax: 01580 200102
Email:	info@pashleymanorgardens.com
Website:	www.pashleymanorgardens.com
Location:	On the B2099 between the A21 and Ticehurst village (Tourist brown-signed).

The National Trust Sheffield Park and Garden — East Sussex

This magnificent informal landscape garden was laid out in the 18th century by 'Capability' Brown and further developed in the early years of the 20th century by its owner Arthur G. Soames. The original four lakes form the centrepiece.

There are dramatic shows of daffodils and bluebells in spring and the rhododendrons and azaleas are spectacular in early summer. Autumn brings stunning colours from the many rare trees and shrubs and winter walks can be enjoyed in this garden for all seasons. Don't forget to visit our newly acquired parkland – perfect for a good walk with stunning views.

Whatever the season, Sheffield Park and Garden offers a fantastic visit for all!

Fact File

Opening times:	Open all year, please telephone or check website for details.
Admission Rates:	Please call 01825 790231 or check our website www.nationaltrust.org.uk/sheffieldpark for current admission rates.
	NT members free. RHS members free, (individual members only)
Group Rates:	(pre-booked), Minimum Group Size: 15.
Guided tour:	£2.50 pp (inc. NT members), (Must be pre-booked)
Facilities:	Visitor Centre, Shop, Plant Sales, Restaurant (not NT) Munch Buggy (NT in garden)
Disabled Access:	Yes. Wheelchair loan available. PMV Loan, Yes booking required, book on 01825 790302
Toilets on site:	Yes
Car Parking on site:	Yes
Coach Parking:	Yes
Guided Tours:	Yes, booking required.
Length of Visit:	2 hours garden 2 hours parkland
Special Events:	Throughout the year - check website for details.
Booking Contact:	Jill Reeves, The National Trust Sheffield Park Garden, Sheffield Park, East Sussex TN22 3QX Booking Tel No.01825 790231, Booking Fax No. 01825 791264
Email:	sheffieldpark.groups@nationaltrust.org.uk
Website:	www.nationaltrust.org.uk/sheffieldpark
Location:	5 miles NW of Uckfield, on east side of A275 (between A272 and A22).

Please quote this guide when making a booking

Arundel Castle Gardens & The Collector Earl's Garden.

The award-winning Collector Earl's Garden, opened in May 2008 by HRH The Prince of Wales, has been conceived as a light-hearted tribute to Thomas Howard, 14th Earl of Arundel (1585-1646), known as 'The Collector'.

Designed by Isabel & Julian Bannerman, the garden includes domed pergolas of green oak, and fountains inspired by the garden vista in the famous Mytens portrait of the Countess of Arundel, while the various gateways and pavilions are based on Inigo Jones' designs.

The grand centrepiece is the rockwork 'mountain' planted with palms and rare ferns to represent another world, supporting a green oak version of 'Oberon's Palace', a fantastic spectacle designed by Inigo Jones. This contains a shell-lined interior with a stalagmite fountain and gilded coronet 'dancing' on top of the jet.

The magnificent new English herbaceous borders and the wild flower garden lead into the ornamental organic vegetable garden.

Fact File

Opening Times:	1st April – 30th October, Tuesdays – Sundays, Bank Holiday Mondays and August Mondays, 10am – 5pm
Admission Rates:	Adult: £7.50, Senior Citizens £7.50, Children: £7.50.
Group Rates:	£7.50 – Group Rates are available for Castle and Gardens combined Tickets
Facilities:	Restaurant, Teas, Coffee Shop, Gift Shop
Disabled Access:	Yes
Toilets on Site:	Yes
Car Parking:	No – Pay & Display opposite main gates
Coach Parking:	No – Pay & Display opposite main gates. Free coach parking for pre-booked groups.
Wheelchair Loan:	Yes (Internal use) – Booking recommended
Length of Visit:	1 - 5 hours
Booking Contact:	Penny Horsfield – Head Guide Arundel Castle, Arundel, West Sussex, BN18 9AB Telephone: 01903 882173 Fax: 01903 884581
Email:	penny.horsfield@arundelcastle.org
Website:	www.arundelcastle.org
Location:	4 miles north of Littlehampton and the south coast, and midway between Chichester and Worthing on the A27. Please follow the brown and white tourist road signs.

Please quote this guide when making a booking

Borde Hill has enhanced the colour and charm of its award winning, Grade II* listed garden, park and woodland to celebrate its 45th anniversary being open to the public. New planting has been undertaken throughout its distinctive 'garden rooms', accentuate elegance and formality of the Italian Garden and increasing the vibrancy of Paradise Walk and sub-tropical Round Dell. The expansion of its well acclaimed Rose Garden to include new 'Gold Standard' rose beds have created a glorious and fragrant botanical display to further delight the senses.

The 17 acres of formal gardens offer a variety of colour in every season. Early spring flowering bulbs, renowned collection of magnolias, camellias, rhododendrons and azaleas give way to exuberant summer borders of roses and herbaceous plants, followed by an autumnal blaze. Beyond, 200 acres of unique woodlands and parkland expand into the distant panorama of the Sussex High Weald, creating spectacular views. Rare tree and shrub species can be found in the microclimates evolving here, along with the largest collection of tallest and widest girth 'champion' trees on private land in Britain.

Fact File

Opening times:	21 March - 11 September 2011 and 22 October – 30 October 2011, daily 10a.m. - 6p.m.
Admission Rates:	Adults: £8.00, Concession: £7.00, Children: £4.75
Facilities:	Shop, Plants Sales, Jeremy's Restaurant, Café Elvira, New Ecological Children's Adventure Playground, Course Fishing
Disabled Access:	Yes, wheelchair loan available (booking required)
Toilets on site:	Yes
Car Parking on site:	Yes
Coach Parking:	Yes
Guided Tours:	Yes, booking required
Length of Visit:	2-4 hours
Special Events:	Easter Bunny Trail 3rd - 25th April, Roses in Bloom 6th - 30th June, Battle Proms 6th August, see website for full programme.
Booking Contact:	Borde Hill Garden, Balcombe Road, Haywards Heath, West Sussex RH16 1XP Booking Tel No. 01444 450326 Booking Fax No. 01444 440427
Email:	info@bordehill.co.uk
Website:	www.bordehill.co.uk

Please quote this guide when making a booking

Especially colourful in spring and autumn, High Beeches is a romantic landscape, changing with the seasons. Discover 27 acres of beautiful and historic woodland and water gardens full of rare and unusual plants and trees. Wander down the winding paths, through open sunlit glades, enjoy stunning vistas and sit by tranquil ponds.

In spring enjoy daffodils along with camellias and many different magnolias, followed by bluebells throughout the woodland glades. The gardens are spectacular in May and early June, carpeted with amazing colour and fragrance from azaleas and magnificent rhododendrons.

The old wildflower meadow is full of wild orchids, cowslips, oxeye daisies and many other wildflowers throughout June and The National Collection of Stewartia flower at the end of June. In August the wonderful azure blue Willow Gentians bloom throughout the glades – High Beeches is the only site in the UK where these have naturalised.

In autumn the views alter again as the varied foliage changes to a splendid crescendo of crimson, copper, gold and green with one of the finest displays of autumnal colour in the country.

Fact File

Opening times:	1 – 5 p.m. every day except Wednesday, 19th March – 30th October
Admission Rates:	Adults: £6.00, Senior Citizens: £6.00, Children: Under 14 – Free
Group Rates:	Minimum Group Size: 20. Adults: £5.50, Senior Citizens: £5.50, Children: Under 14 – Free
Facilities:	Restaurant, Teas
Disabled Access:	Limited – tearoom yes
Toilets on site:	Yes
Car Parking on site:	Yes
Coach Parking:	Yes
Guided Tours:	Yes, booking required.
Length of Visit:	2 hours
Special Events:	See website.
Booking Contact:	Sarah Bray, High Beeches Gardens, Handcross, West Sussex RH17 6HQ Booking Tel No. 01444 400589. Booking Fax No. 01444 401543
Email:	gardens@highbeeches.com
Website:	www.highbeeches.com
Location:	1 mile east of the A223 at Handcross on the south side of the B2110 in mid-Sussex.

Please quote this guide when making a booking

In the late 1800s, an unusually creative family bought the Nymans estate in the picturesque Sussex Weald to make a home in the country. Inspired by the setting and the soil, the Messels created one of the greatest gardens, with experimental designs and new plants from around the world. In their home they entertained family and friends, enjoyed relaxing in the garden, playing and picnicking, and walking in the woods. You can enjoy Nymans in the same way they did. We are reinventing Nymans for the 21st century by working the estate in a new, greener way.

Fact File

Opening Times: Garden, Woods, Restaurant, Shop & Plant Centre, January 1st - February 28th 10-4pm, Monday to Sunday. March 1st - October 31st 10-5pm, Monday to Sunday. November 1st - December 24 10-4pm, Monday to Sunday. House, March 2nd - October 31st 11-3pm, all week except Tuesdays.

Admission Rates: Gift Aid - Adult £9.50, Child £5.00, Family 2 Adults + 3, £24.00, Family 1 Adult + 3 £14.50. Standard - Adult £8.50, Child £4.50, Family 2 Adults + 3, £21.50, Family 1 Adult + 3 £13.00. National Trust members FREE

Group Rates: 15+, Adult £8.00, Child £4.00.

Facilities: Visitor Centre, shop, plant sales, restaurant, teas.

Disabled Access: Yes, wheelchair loan available, Toilets on site.

Tours/Events: Guided tours, trails and iPod audio guides available from the information point. Mobility buggy tours of garden and woods. Events include family activities, open-air theatre, gardening workshops, woodland wildlife walks.

Parking: Yes, coach and car parking available.

Length of Visit: 3 hours

Booking Contact: Nymans Administrator, Booking Telephone No. 01444 405250

Email: nymans@nationaltrust.org.uk **Website:** www.nationaltrust.org.uk/nymans

Location: 5 miles south of Crawley. Foot: 5 miles by footpath from Balcombe. Cycle: on the National Cycle Network route 20. Ferry: Dieppe or Le Harvre to Newhaven, then 40 mins by car / train. Bus: Metrobus 273 Brighton to Crawley, 271 Haywards Heath to Crawley. Both stop outside Nymans. Both pass Crawley . Train: Balcombe 4 miles, Crawley 5 miles. Road: on B2114 at Handcross, just off London to Brighton M23/A23. Parking: free. Designated coach bays.

Please quote this guide when making a booking

One of the top twenty in Simon Jenkins' book "England's Thousand Best Houses", Parham is one of England's finest Elizabethan examples. Set in the heart of a deer park, with its dark fallow herd first recorded in 1628, the house sits below a completely unspoilt stretch of the South Downs. Its Pleasure Grounds, laid out in the 18th century, encompass specimen trees, a brick and turf maze built in 1991. They lead down to a peaceful lake overlooked by a summer house.

The spectacular four-acre walled garden, cultivated for many centuries, contains herbaceous and mixed borders of Edwardian opulence. Vibrant with colour, it is run on organic principles and designed for a long season, peaking in summer and in late autumn. With its herbs, vegetables, lavender, roses and fruit trees, the garden is a series of interlocking pictures, woven into each other with a tapestry-like effect in the English romantic tradition.

The Wendy House, built into the old garden wall, with its balcony, fireplace and parquet floor, was built in 1928 for the daughters of the Hon. Clive and Alicia Pearson, who bought the estate in 1922.

Parham is justly famous for its long tradition of flower arrangements which decorate every room in the house. Everything is cut from the garden, which won the HHA/Christie's Garden of the Year Award in 1990.

Fact File

Opening Times:	3rd April to 29th september 2011, Wednesdays, Thursdays, Sundays & Bank Holiday Mondays, also Tuesdays & Fridays in August 2pm - 5pm. Gardens: Wednesdays, Thursdays, Sundays & Bank Holiday Mondays also Tuesdays and Fridays between May and August 12 noon - 5pm.
Admission Rates:	See web site for 2011 rates.
Group Rates:	Discounted rates for group advanced bookings.
Facilities:	Restaurant, Gift Shop, Picnic Area, Plant Sales, Shop, Brick & Turf Maze, Wendy House.
Disabled Access:	Yes. Toilet and parking for disabled on site.
Tours/Events:	Garden Weekend, 9th, 10th July 2011. A Celebration of Spring, 10th April 2011.
Coach Parking:	Yes. No Charge.
Length of Visit:	1 - 2 hours (excluding house)
Booking Contact:	Parham House & Gardens, Storrington, Pulborough, West Sussex, RH20 4HS. Telephone: 01903 742021 or 744888 (information line) Fax: 01903 746557.
Email:	bookings@parhaminsussex.co.uk
Website:	www.parhaminsussex.co.uk
Location:	Parham is located on the A283 midway between Storrington and Pulborough, Equidistant from the A24 or A29.

Please quote this guide when making a booking

In the heart of the South Downs National Park.
A short lime avenue leads to the Topiary Garden with its amusing animals and birds in clipped box and yew. Beyond the stone balustraded bridge a riot of hollyhocks can be seen in high summer in front of the 15th century timber-framed house. Here visitors can still see the fine panelled interiors of a much-loved home.

Through the stone arch the yew tunnel leads to the mysterious ivy-clad Monks' Walk. The upper lawn is enclosed by herbaceous borders, while the lower lawn has clipped yew hedges and roses, with an exceptional example of the 'Living Fossil' tree, the prehistoric *Ginkgo Biloba*.

The five acres of gardens include the Victorian 'Secret' Garden, with its 40-metre fruit wall, heated pineapple pits and stove house. The Victorian potting shed now houses a Rural Museum of horticultural implements from the family farms. The Rose Garden commemorates the Queen's Golden Jubilee. The Terracotta Garden has a central fountain, complemented by colourful herbaceous borders. The unusual English Poetry Garden, in its semi-woodland setting, has a bust of lord Byron as its centrepiece, a long curved pergola, and poems displayed around the circular broadwalk for the pleasure of visitors.

Fact File

Opening Times:	May to end of September (House and Gardens). Public open afternoons Suns, Thurs, BH Mondays 2-6pm (last entry 5pm). Groups at other times by appointment.
Admission Rates:	House and Gardens: Adults £7.50, Concession £6.50, Child £4.00. Gardens only: Adults £5.00, Concession £4.00, Child £2.50.
Group Rates:	Groups (of 25 or more). House and Gardens: £7.00, Gardens only: £4.50.
Facilities:	Gift Shop, Teas, Car Park.
Disabled Access:	Partial.
Tours/Events:	Guided tours of House and Gardens for groups.
Coach Parking:	Yes.
Length of Visit:	2 - 3 hours.
Booking Contact:	Jean Whitaker St Mary's House, Bramber, West Sussex, BN44 3WE. Tel: 01903 816205 Fax: 01903 816205
Email:	info@stmarysbramber.co.uk
Website:	www.stmarysbramber.co.uk
Location:	10 miles NW of Brighton off A283 in Bramber Village, 1 mile east of Steyning.

Please quote this guide when making a booking

Although Ragley's 400 acres of parkland were designed by Lancelot 'Capability' Brown during the 18th Century, little is known about the gardens prior to 1873 when Victorian garden designer Robert Marnock created a formal flower garden intended to show off plants discovered in the new world.

This area of the garden is now a modern Rose Garden, completed in 2009, with the new design based around diversity by taking away the majority of the grass and planting trees, shrubs and perennials to encourage insects. This naturalistic approach is demonstrated throughout the Gardens which provide colour and interest throughout the year with areas such as a Spring Bulb Bank, Prairie Garden and Alpine Garden.

Other attractions at Ragley include a Woodland Walk, which takes visitors around the surrounding Parkland and provides some wonderful views of the countryside, a collection of 19th Century Carriages housed in the Stables and, of course, the Palladian House itself.

Fact File

Opening times:	Please see website or contact us on 01789 762090 for details.
Admission Rates:	Please see website or contact us on 01789 762090 for details.
Group Rates:	Please see website or contact us on 01789 762090 for details.
Facilities:	Teas, Light Refreshments
Disabled Access:	Yes. Wheelchair loan available – booking required
Toilets on site:	Yes
Car Parking on site:	Yes
Coach Parking:	Yes
Guided Tours:	Yes, booking required.
Length of Visit:	2 hours for gardens, plus further 2 hours to visit woodland walk and house
Booking Contact:	Carol Handy, Ragley Hall, Alcester Warwickshire, B49 5NJ
	Booking Tel No.01789 762090, Booking Fax No. 01789 768691
Email:	ragley@ragleyhall.com
Website:	www.ragleyhall.com
Location:	Ragley is situated 2 miles southwest of Alcester, off the A435/A46

Please quote this guide when making a booking

Ryton Gardens   Warwickshire

Ryton Gardens is home to Garden Organic, the UK's leading organic growing charity showcasing ten acres of stunning organic display gardens. These demonstrate all aspects of domestic horticulture including herbs, roses, lawns, shrubberies, herbaceous planting and vegetable and fruit growing.

The gardens are full of information for gardeners on organic techniques including composting and pest and disease control. The grounds also boast a large conservation area with native trees and wild flowers, a bee garden, living willow structures and the world's first public biodynamic garden.

The Vegetable Kingdom, an interactive visitor centre, houses Garden Organic's world renowned Heritage Seed Library which conserves hundreds of threatened vegetable varieties.

The site is also home to an award winning restaurant and shop where organic, local and sustainable produce, including delicious home cooked food, gifts and products, are available to buy.

Fact File

Opening Times:	9am - 5pm all year round
Admission Rates:	Adults £6.00 (admits 1 child free), Concessions £5.50, £3.00 for additional child, members go free.
Facilities:	Visitor centre, award winning shop & restaurant, garden café, plant sales, picnic area, large car park.
Disabled Access:	Disabled toilet and parking facilities. Wheelchairs available – booking necessary. Braille Guidebook.
Tours/Events:	Annual programme of events. Garden tours and group visits available to book.
Coach Parking:	Yes.
Length of Visit:	Half a day
Booking Contact:	Garden Organic, Ryton Gardens, Wolston Lane, Coventry, CV8 3LG. Telephone: 02476 303517 Fax: 02476 639229
Email:	enquiry@gardenorganic.org.uk
Website:	www.gardenorganic.org.uk
Location:	Just off the A45 on the road to Wolston, five miles south east of Coventry.

Beside the Abbey Church in Malmesbury and straddling the River Avon, this truly spectacular 5 acre garden has brought praise from around the world.

These are just some of the comments from our visitors' book:

"I thought I'd seen all the best gardens in the world – until now!"
"The loveliest truly English garden on the planet!"
"This garden alone made my visit to the UK worthwhile"

With over 1000 years of history, burial place of an English King, knot gardens, herb gardens, river walk, monastic fishponds, waterfall over 2000 different roses (largest collection in the UK) over 100,000 tulips, 10,000 different plants with constant colour from March to November, these 5 acres are a must see garden and history experience with approx. half an hour drive from Bath.

p.s. you can even get married here!

Fact File

Opening Times:	11am - 5.30pm 21st March - 31st October
Admission Rates:	Adults £7.00, Concessions £6.00, Children £3.00
Group Rates:	Minimum Group Size: 20. £5.50 per person.
Facilities:	Plant Sales, Teas.
Disabled Access:	Yes.
Tours/Events:	Plays, Demonstrations, Sculpture and Exhibitions. Also licensed for Civil Marriage/Partnerships, See website for additional information.
Coach Parking:	Yes.
Length of Visit:	2 hours minimum
Booking Contact:	Geraldine Wilkins. Abbey House Gardens, Market Cross, Malmesbury, Wiltshire, SN16 9AS Tel: 01666 827650, Fax: 01666 822782
Email:	info@abbeyhousegardens.co.uk
Website:	www.abbeyhousegardens.co.uk
Location:	In Malmesbury town centre. Off A429 between M4 junction 17 (5miles) and Cirencester (12 miles). Coaches drop passengers in centre of town, 3 minute level walk from garden. Cars follow signs for long stay car park from Malmesbury town centre. Garden is 5 min walk across the bridge, up the Abbey steps and entered left of Cloister Garden.

Please quote this guide when making a booking

Bowood Rhododendron Woodland Garden   Wiltshire

Bowood Gardens and Grounds are open from April to November. However, the Rhododendron Woodland Garden (accessed via a separate entrance off the A342) is only open for six weeks, from late April to early June.

The formal terraces in front of the House are a riot of colour throughout the season. Thousands of Tulips herald the arrival of spring, followed by Alliums, Geraniums and Roses. A breathtaking new border which is seventy metres long and four metres deep, designed by Rosie Abel Smith, our Garden Consultant, runs parallel with the main lawn. This herbaceous border has won accolades from all who visit. For groups of twenty or more, guided tours of the four acre private walled garden are now available by prior appointment. This garden is divided into four one acre squares: formal borders, picking garden, fruit & vegetables and glass houses.

The Rhododendron Woodland Garden, covering sixty acres, surrounds Robert Adam's Palladian Mausoleum built in 1762. In late April, the under storey is carpeted with bluebells. Towering above are magnificent scented Loderi and Kewensis, with huge pink trusses, followed in May and June by some of the earliest known hardy hybrids introduced in 1854.

Fact File

Opening Times:	Terraces and Pleasure Grounds 11.00 – 18.00 1st April – 30th October
	Rhododendron Walk 11.00 – 18.00 Mid April – early June
Admissions Rates:	Terraces and Pleasure Grounds: Adults £9.50, Senior Citizens £8.00, Children £5.00.
	Rhododendron Walk Adults: £6.00, Senior Citizens £5.50
	Combined ticket Adults: £13.50, Senior Citizens: £11.50
Facilities:	Terraces and Pleasure Grounds, Coffee shop, gift shop, restaurant, picnic area, Rhododendron Walk, Toilets.
Disabled Access:	Limited, bookable wheelchair loan available.
Tours and Events:	Pre-booked guided tours of the Private Gardens are available minimum numbers apply .
Coach Parking:	Yes.
Length of Visit:	Minimum of 2 hours.
Booking Contact:	Katrina Druit, Bowood House, Calne, Wiltshire, SN11 0LZ
	Telephone: 01249 812102 Fax: 01249 821757
Email:	houseandgardens@bowood.org
Website:	www.bowood.org
Location:	Off A 342 between Derry Hill and Sandy Lane. 8 miles south of Junction 17, M4.

Please quote this guide when making a booking

Alfred Parsons designed Arts and Crafts gardens to complement restoration of the manor in 1905-1912. He kept the large lawn but designed terraces, walls, flagged paths, topiary pavilions beside a lily pond, and cedar over a gazebo with swept roof in local stone: creating subtle frameworks for the future.

Snowdrops and aconites sparkle around the springfed lower moat; daffodils, tulips and Queen Anne's lace follow in the orchard. A charming rill is fed from the upper moat or mill pond. Roses flourish: Caroline Testout and Bennetts' Seedling in the forecourt, Old Blush China in the churchyard, Natalie Nyples surrounds the well, Rambling Rector and Sanders White climb in apples, and The Fairy tumbles in profusion to the lower moat.

In autumn asters flower below the terrace, Virginia creeper then willows flame at the entrance. Robert Fuller gave his Manor to the National Trust in 1943, it is now home to his grandson's family who have replanted the gardens. The house and garden feature in the film 'The Other Boleyn Girl'.

Fact File

Opening Times:	Garden open Tuesday, Wednesdays, Thursday, 11am - 5pm. April - October. Manor Admission by guided tour Tuesday – Thursday 11, 12, 2, 3 & 4. Sunday: Garden open 2pm – 5pm. Manor tours at 2, 3 & 4. April - October.
Admission Rates:	Adults: £7.60 (Garden only: £4.80) Senior Citizens: N/A, Children: £3.80 (Garden only: £2.40), Family: £19.40
Group Rates:	Minimum Group Size: 15 Adults: £6.50, Senior Citizens: N/A, Children: £3.20
Disabled Access:	No – photo album available. Garden partly accessible. Car parking and toilet on site.
Tours/Events:	Yes.
Coach Parking:	Drop-off point
Length of Visit:	Whole visit: 1 hour, 30 minutes.
Booking Contact:	Mrs. R. Floyd Great Chalfield Manor & Garden. Nr. Melksham, Wiltshire SN12 8NH Tel: 01225 782239
Email:	greatchalfieldmanor@nationaltrust.org.uk
Website:	www.nationaltrust.org.uk/greatchalfieldmanor
Location:	3 miles south-west of Melksham, off B3107, via Broughton Gifford Common.

Please quote this guide when making a booking

Romantically sited overlooking the valley of the River Frome, close to Bradford-on-Avon, Iford Manor is built into the hillside below a hanging beechwood and fine garden terraces. The house was owned during the first part of the last century by Harold Peto, the architect and landscape designer who taught Lutyens, and who expressed his passion for classical Italian architecture and landscaping in an English setting. After many visits to Italy he acquired statues and architectural marbles. He planted phillyrea and cypress trees and other Mediterranean species to add to the plantings of the eighteenth century and to enhance the Italian character of the garden.

The great terrace is bounded on one side by an elegant colonnade and commands lovely views out over the orchard and the surrounding countryside. Paths wander through the Woodland and garden to the summerhouse, the cloister and the casita and amongst the water features.

Fact File

Opening Times: 2pm - 5pm Sundays April and October.
2pm - 5pm Tuesdays - Thursdays, Saturday, Sunday and Bank Holiday Mondays, May to September. Mornings and Mondays and Fridays reserved for group visits by Appointment.

Admission Rates: Adults £5.00, Senior Citizen £4.50, Child under 10 free.

Group Rates: Minimum group size: 8
Adults £5.50, Senior Citizen £5.50, Child under 10 free for visits outside normal hours.

Facilities: House Keeper's Cream Teas at weekends. Cake "du jour" on weekdays. Group refreshments by arrangement.

Disabled Access: Yes, Toilet and parking for disabled on site.

Tours/Events: By appointment

Coach Parking: Yes.

Length of Visit: 1-1½ hours

Booking Contact: Mrs Elizabeth Cartwright-Hignett
Iford Manor, Bradford on Avon, Wiltshire BA15 2BA
Telephone: 01225 863146 Fax: 01225 862364

Website: www.ifordmanor.co.uk

Location: Follow brown tourist signs to Iford Manor:- 7 miles south of Bath on A36 Warminster Road & ½ mile south of Bradford on Avon on B3109.

Please quote this guide when making a booking

A garden of immense charm, peacefulness and quiet colours, created from scratch over the past 40 years.

In spring many Magnolias, bulbs, Deutzias and Elaeagnus create a paradise of white, pale shades of pink and primrose yellow. Glorious scents fill the air. June sees the climax of the 130 old-fashioned roses, species roses and ramblers, some cascading from the tops of trees. Gently sloping lawns are edged by mixed borders. The 3 acre wild flower meadow acts as a magnet for butterflies.

Many treasures are to be found here, including white Martagon lilies, Fritillaries, Tree peonies and over 20 Daphnes. The young arboretum contains 38 different forms of Oak, as well as many cultivars of Beech, Tulip trees and a collection of Maples, to name but a few of the 4000 trees planted since 1988. Autumn colours grow richer each year above carpets of wild Cyclamen hederifolium.

There is a potager, with clipped box shapes and a productive kitchen garden and walnut grove.

Plants propagated from the garden are offered for sale.

Fact File

Opening times:	Garden open throughout the year by appointment only. Please telephone 01225 891204
Admission Rates:	Adults £6.00, Senior Citizens £6.00, Children under 14 - Free
Group Rates:	No minimum but guided tours minimum spend of £50 -, Adults £6.50 (Guided) £5.50 (Unguided), Senior Citizens £6.50 (Guided) £5.50 (Unguided), Children under 14 - Free
Facilities:	Homemade teas and lunches by appointment, Plant Sales
Disabled Access:	Yes
Toilets on Site:	Yes
Car Parking:	Yes
Coach Parking:	Yes (by prior appointment)
Wheelchair Loan:	N/A
Length of Visit:	1 – 2 hours. Guided tours can be done by owners – booking required
Booking Contact:	Sue Young Ridleys Cheer, Mountain Bower, Chippenham, Wiltshire, SN14 7AJ Telephone: 01225 891204
Email:	sueyoung@ridleyscheer.co.uk
Website:	www.ridleyscheer.co.uk
Location:	1 mile north of A420 Chippenham – Bristol Road. Turn north at The Shoe, (signed Grittleton) then 2nd left and first right.

Please quote this guide when making a booking

Often referred to as "Paradise", Stourhead is an exquisite example of an English landscape garden. It was once described by Horace Walpole as 'one of the most picturesque scenes in the world'.

Visitors can discover the inspiration behind Henry Hoare II's world famous garden, laid out between 1741 and 1780 and enjoy breathtaking views all year round.

The garden is dotted with Classical temples including the Pantheon and the Temple of Apollo, which provide a dramatic backdrop to the majestic lake, secluded valley and magnificent trees.

Stourhead House, an 18th century Palladian Mansion, is situated at the top of the gardens surrounded by lawns and parkland.

The Stourhead Estate extends east to King Alfred's Tower, a 160 foot folly 2½ miles from the House which affords stunning views across three counties, and is the perfect place for picnics. Visitors can also enjoy breathtaking walks across Whitesheet Hill's chalk downs, and explore the mature woodland packed with an exciting range of trees, and a rich array of native wildlife.

Fact File

Opening Times: Garden open all year daily 9am-7pm.
House open Friday-Tuesday 13th March-31st October, 11am-5pm, last entry 4.30pm
King Alfred's Tower open daily, 13th March-31st October, 11am-5pm, last entry 4.30pm.

Admission Rates: Garden & House: Adults £12.80*, Child £6.40*. Garden or House: Adults £7.70*, Child £4.20*.
King Alfred's Tower: Adult £3.10*, Child: £1.60*. National Trust members free.
Includes a voluntary 10% donation but visitors can however, choose to pay the standard prices which are displayed at the property and on the website.

Group Rates: Minimum group size 15: Garden & House £11.20, Garden or House £6.70.
King Alfred's Tower £2.60. National Trust members free.

Facilities: Visitor Centre, Shop, Plant Centre, Self-service Restaurant, Farm Shop, Spread Eagle Inn, Art Gallery, Ice Cream Parlour, Licensed Civil Ceremony venue.

Disabled Access: Toilets, parking, Shuttle Bus service March to October. Sympathetic hearing scheme, Assistance dogs welcome and wheelchairs. Self-drive mobility vehicle subject to availability. Stair-climber available with advance booking.

Tours/Events: Please contact us for details of all our events and tours.

Coach Parking: Yes.

Length of Visit: Recommend Minimum 3 hours.

Booking Contact: Georgina Mead. Stourhead Estate Office, Stourton, Nr Mere, Warminster, Wiltshire BA12 6QD
Tel: 01747 841152 Fax: 01747 842005

Email: stourhead@nationaltrust.org.uk

Website: www.nationaltrust.org.uk/stourhead

Location: Stourhead is in the village of Stourton, off the B3092, 3 miles northwest of Mere (A303) or 8 miles south of Frome (A361).

Please quote this guide when making a booking

Arley Arboretum is one of the oldest privately owned arboretums in Great Britain. It boasts more than 300 species of trees in formal and informal plantings and gardens. Nestling in the Severn Valley and overlooking the river, it has been growing and maturing in this idyllic setting for two centuries.

Spring in Arley is a magical time of growth and renewal. A carpet of spring flowering bulbs drives away the winter gloom. The arboretum is filled with birdsong and the bustling activity of its many residents. Explore the stunning Magnolia garden and enjoy the Azaleas and Rhododendrons in bloom. In summer the herbaceous borders in the walled garden and the planters in the Italian garden are a riot of colour.

Autumn is a wonderful time of year in the arboretum. The leaves turn a kaleidoscope of colours, and cover the ground with a rich and exotic carpet. Visitors can enjoy the spectacle of the acers in their autumn glory and the Barbican Tower with its scarlet waistcoat and fine display provided throughout the arboretum.

Fact File

Opening Times: Wednesday to Sunday 11 a.m. – 5 p.m.
Admission Rates: Adults: £6.00, Senior Citizens: £6.00, Children aged 3-16: £2.00.
Group Rates: Minimum Group Size: 10. Adults: £5.50. Senior Citizens: £5.50, Children: £2.00.
RHS Members Free on Thursdays only.
Facilities: Tea room, open to non visitors.
Disabled Access: Yes.
Toilet On Site: Yes.
Tours/Events: Yes. Booking required.
Coach Parking: Yes.
Car Parking: Yes.
Length of Visit: Minimum 1½ hours to all day.
Booking Contact: Mrs. Norah Howells
Arley Arboretum & Gardens, Arley estate Office, Upper Arley, Nr. Bewdley, Worcs. DY12 1XG
Booking Telephone No. 01299 861368
Email: info@arley-arboretum.org.uk
Website: www.arley-arboretum.org.uk
Location: Between Kidderminster and Bridgnorth on the A442 and is brown-signed from this road.

Please quote this guide when making a booking

Spetchley Park Gardens

Worcestershire

This is a beautiful 30 acre Victorian garden, surrounded by glorious countryside and boasting an enviable collection of worldwide plant treasures. You can enjoy the fantastic vistas and stunning architecture that not only inspired Edward Elgar to write one of his great compositions from the gardener's cottage but was also home to convalescing American pilots during World War 2

The wonderful display of spring bulbs in April and May, together with flowering trees and shrubs are followed in June and July by the large selection of roses, whilst July, August and September reveal the great herbaceous borders in all their glory. This is a garden for all seasons

Having explored the gardens you can enjoy the peaceful surroundings of the Tea room or, for the more adventurous walk around the 150 acre deer park with its herd of red and fallow deer.

Fact File

Opening times:	21st March - 30th September. Wednesday - Sunday 11am - 6pm, 1st - 31st October. Saturdays and Sundays 11am - 4pm. Bank Holiday Mondays 11am - 6pm. Last admissions one hour before closing.
Admission Rates:	Adults £6.00, Senior Citizen £5.50, Under 16s free. Adults Season Tickets £25.00
Group Rates:	Minimum group size: 25 Adults £5.00, Senior Citizen £5.00, Child £1.90.
Facilities:	Tea Room, plant sales and small gift shop.
Disabled Access:	Partial. Parking for disabled on site, Booking necessary for parties. (Access restricted, please telephone contact details below for advice).
Tours/Events:	Please check website for details.
Coach Parking:	Yes.
Length of Visit:	2 hours minimum.
Booking Contact:	Berkeley Estate Office, Ham, Berkeley, Gloucestershire GL13 9QL. Tel: 01453 810303 Fax: 01453 511915
Email:	hb@spetchleygardens.co.uk
Website:	www.spetchleygardens.co.uk
Location:	2 miles east of Worcester on A44, leave M5 at either junctions 6 or 7

Please quote this guide when making a booking

A haven for flower lovers with 14 acres packed full of over 4,000 different varieties of perennials and 2,000 shrubs and trees. The gardens have been designed through careful successional planting to be at their best throughout the summer with particular highlights including in May and June our large collections of oriental poppies, irises and peonies, followed in mid-summer by roses, daylilies and alstroemerias and by late summer asters, crocosmias and sedums.

Features include extensive herbaceous borders, rock garden, fragrant rose garden, annual meadow, cottage garden, special June and September gardens and much more .....

2011 will see the opening of our new cafe for light lunches, tea, coffee and cakes etc. (Thursday to Sunday only) Also, our specialist perennial nursery sells a wide range of rare and unusual plants your neighbours won't have, all of which can be seen growing in the gardens.

Fact File

Opening Times:	May 22nd – September 30th, 11am – 5pm daily
Admission Rates:	Adults £4.00, Senior Citizen £4.00, Children under 16 Free
Group Rates:	As above.
Facilities:	Cafe (open Thursday to Sunday only), Plant Sales.
Disabled Access:	Yes
Tours Events:	Guided Tours and Group Bookings by appointment.
Coach Parking:	Yes
Length of Visit:	1½ - 2 hours for the Gardens
Booking Contact:	Marylen Parker
	Breezy Knees Gardens, Common Lane, Warthill, York, YO19 5XS
	Telephone: 01904 488800
Email:	N/A
Website:	www.breezyknees.co.uk
Location:	5 miles east of York, 1 mile off A64 between A64 and Warthill village

Burton Agnes Hall & Gardens

Winners of 2005 HHA Christies Garden of the Year Award

Burton Agnes is a magnificent Elizabethan Hall surrounded by lawns, topiary yew bushes and beautiful award winning gardens. The eastern aspect of the house showcases a classical pond with beautiful fountains and a newly created pebble mosaic. To the right of the house lies an Elizabethan walled garden, home to over 3,000 different plants, a potager of herbs and vegetables, fruit beds and even a maze! Contained within the walled garden is also a National Collection of campanulas, a fantastic knot garden with coloured theme gardens and giant board games.

Fact File

Opening Times:	Gardens, shops and cafe open 5th - 27th February, daily 11am to 4pm
	Hall, gardens, shops and cafe open 1st April to 31st October, daily 11am to 5pm
	Christmas Opening 14th November to 22nd December, daily 11am to 5pm
Admission Rates:	Adults £5.00, Senior Citizens £4.50, Children £3.00
Group rates:	10% discount for groups of 30+
Facilities:	Elizabethan Hall and gardens with courtyard shops, cafe and plant sales
Disabled Access:	Yes, toilet and parking on site.
Tours/Events:	Guided tours available on request.
	Snowdrop Opening 5th-27th Feb
	Orchid Weekend 5th & 6th March
	Easter Egg Hunt 24th & 25th April
	Gardeners' Fair 11th and 12th June
	Michaelmas Fair 29th and 30st October
	Christmas Opening 14th Nov - 22nd Dec
Coach Parking:	Yes
Length of Visit:	1 1/2 to 2 hours
Booking Contact:	The Estate Office, Burton Agnes Hall, Burton Agnes, Near Driffield, East Yorks, YO25 4NB. Telephone: 01262 490324
Email:	office@burtonagnes.com
Website:	www.burtonagnes.com
Location:	On A614 between Driffield and Bridlington.

Please quote this guide when making a booking

Fountains Abbey and Studley Royal Water Garden North Yorkshire

Yorkshire's first World Heritage site is a truly remarkable place encompassing nearly 900 years of history.

Once wild and wooded, this landscape was transformed into one of England's most spectacular Georgian water gardens by the Aislabie family. Conserved to look much as it would in the 18th century, this elegant ornamental garden is adorned with neo-classical statues, temples and follies which appear reflected in long mirror-like stretches of water. Take in the formal geometric design with beautifully contrived vistas, majestic sweeping avenues and breathtaking surprise views. Let yourself be transported to another era where peace and tranquillity reign.

The perfect complement to the garden is 12th century Fountains Abbey, landscaped into the garden as the ultimate surprise view. Lose yourself in the passages, staircases and towers of the largest, best-preserved monastic ruins in the country, and marvel at a unique relic of ancient craftsmanship

Fact File

Opening Times:	April - Sept 10am - 5pm, October - March 10am - 4pm. Closed Fridays in November - January and closed 24th and 25th December.
Admission Rates:	Adults £9.00, Child £4.85, Family's £23.00, NT/EH Members Free. Under 5's Free.
Groups Rates:	Group discounts and bespoke tours available, call the Group Visits Organiser on 01765 643197.
Facilities:	Shop, Tea Room, Restaurant, Kiosk and Play Area.
Disabled Access:	Yes. Toilet and parking for disabled on site. Personal Mobility Vehicles on loan, booking necessary.
Tours/Events:	Guided Tours for groups, must be pre booked, telephone 01765 643197. Annual events programme, please enqire for details.
Coach Parking:	Yes
Length of Visit:	1½ hours minimum.
Booking Contact:	Fountains Abbey, Ripon, Yorkshire, HG4 3DY Telephone: 01765 608888 Fax: 01765 601002
Email:	fountainsabbey@nationaltrust.org.uk
Website:	www.fountainsabbey.org.uk www.nationaltrust.org.uk
Location:	4 miles west of Ripon of B6265 to Pateley Bridge, signposted from A1, 10 miles north of Harrogate A61.

Please quote this guide when making a booking

RHS Garden Harlow Carr

One of Yorkshire's most relaxing and surprising gardens at the gateway to the Yorkshire Dales!

Wander through tranquil surroundings in this stunning garden and pick up the latest tips and techniques for your own borders.

In the spring you can look forward to the riotous bulb displays which bring welcome colour and scent to the garden. The dramatic colour then moves to the flower borders in May right through to late summer. Autumn sees the garden transform into its most colourful season. Ablaze with vibrant shrubs and berries, the turning leaves set the whole garden alight in bright red', gold's and amber's.

Highlights include the lush Streamside Garden, take inspiration from 200 years of gardening in Gardens through Time. Pick up practical ideas from the Kitchen Garden and take glorious deep breaths in the beautiful scented garden. Our new Alpine House is not to be missed, as it is the largest of any of the RHS Gardens and is home to a selection of the Harlow Carr Alpine collection made up of over 2000 plants. Visit the extensive RHS Shop & Plant Centre, and linger over delicious goodies in Bettys Café Tea Rooms.

All in all, a truly surprising and entertaining day out!

Fact File

Opening Times:	9.30am - 6pm (4pm Nov - March)
Admission Rates:	Adults £7.50, Child (6-16yrs) £3.00 (under 6's Free). RHS Members (+1 Family guest) Free.
Groups Rates:	Minimum group size 10, (Pre-booking required) £6.50.
Facilities:	Largest Gardening Bookshop in the north, Bettys Cafe Tea Rooms, RHS Gift Shop & Plant Centre, Library.
Disabled Access:	Yes. Toilet and parking for disabled on site. Wheelchairs on loan, booking necessary.
On The Website:	A full programme of events is available from the gardens or from the website.
Coach Parking:	Yes
Length of Visit:	2 hours
Booking Contact:	The Admin Department RHS Garden Harlow Carr, Crag Lane, Harrogate, HG3 1QB Tel: 01423 565418 Fax: 01423 530663
Email:	harlowcarr@rhs.org.uk
Website:	www.rhs.org.uk/harlowcarr
Location:	RHS Garden Harlow Carr is located just two miles from the centre of Harrogate with good links from the town bus and train stations. Take the B6162 Otley Road out of Harrogate towards Beckwithshaw. Harlow Carr is 1.5 miles on the right.

Please quote this guide when making a booking

Helmsley Walled Garden Yorkshire

Set against the backdrop of Helmsley Castle and Duncombe Park, the five acre garden, originally built in 1756, has recently benefited from 15 years of extensive restoration.

The Double Hot Border forms the garden's central spine, extending for 120m, it explodes with colour from June to September

Off the main spine we have a selection of smaller garden rooms including a contemplative garden, a white garden, rose and peony borders and new for 2011 a cottage flower garden.

The garden has dedicated vegetable and trained fruit growing areas, half of which are individually tended by residents of the local community, the remainder grown by ourselves and used exclusively in our award winning vegetarian Vinehouse Cafe.

The range of Victorian greenhouses house a collection of vines, tomatoes and hot house plants.

The garden is a registered charity providing horticultural therapy for the local community.

Fact File

Opening times:	Open 1st April until 31st October 2011, daily 10:30am until 5pm (last admission at 4:30pm)
Admission Rates:	Adult £5.00, Senior Citizens £4.00, Children under 16 free when accompanied by an adult.
Group Rates:	Minimum group size 8 people.
	Adult £4.00, Senior Citizens £3.00, Children under 16 free when accompanied by an adult.
Facilities:	Toilets, Shop, Plant Sales, Vegetarian Cafe
Disabled Access:	Yes. Wheelchairs available booking required.
Tours:	Guided tours available booking required.
Events:	See website for details.
Car/Coach Parking:	Pay and display coach/car park 200m from entrance.
Length of Visit:	2 hours
Booking Contact:	Lindsay Tait. Helmsley Walled Garden, Cleveland Way, Helmsley, North Yorkshire. YO62 5AH Telephone: 01439 771427 Fax: 01439 771427
Email:	Info@helmsleywalledgarden.org.uk
Website:	www.helmsleywalledgarden.org.uk
Location:	Helmsley is situated 25 miles north of York (on the A170), 14 miles from Thirsk and 16 miles from Malton. Follow the signposts from the Cleveland Way car park in Helmsley, located on the north side of the castle. There is free parking for coaches in Cleveland Way coach park.

Please quote this guide when making a booking

Newby Hall's award winning gardens, created in the early 1920s, have evolved over the years making a major contribution to 20th century gardening. They provide a haven for both specialist and amateur gardeners alike. Designed astride one of Europe's longest double herbaceous borders which slopes gently down from the house to the River Ure, are numerous compartmented gardens – 'rooms' off a long corridor. Visit Newby in the Spring, Summer or Autumn and discover the secrets of Sylvia's Garden, the Rose Garden, Autumn Garden or the Water Garden and even a Tropical Garden. Newby also holds the national collection of CORNUS (dogwoods). It is quite simply an experience that no garden-lover should miss.

Fact File

Opening Times:	1 April – 25 September 2011 Tue-Sun and Bank Holidays. 7 days a week in July & August. Gardens open 11am – 5.30pm. House open for guided tours only 12noon – 4pm
Admission Rates:	Adults: House & Gardens £12.00, Gardens Only £8.50, Senior Citizens: House & Gardens £11.00, Gardens Only £7.50, Children: House & Gardens £9.50, Gardens Only £7.00 RHS Members Free - Gardens only, April, May and September
Group Rates:	Minimum Group Size 15, Adults/Seniors: House & Gardens £10.50, Gardens Only £7.00, Children : House & Gardens £8.00, Gardens Only £6.00
Facilities:	Large adventure playground, Miniature railway.
Tours:	Booking Required in advance for groups, on arrival for individuals.
Events:	Spring Plant Fair Sunday 8 May, Craft Fair 3 - 5 June.
Disabled Access:	Yes.
Toilets on Site:	Yes.
Car/Coach Parking:	Yes.
Wheelchair Loan:	Yes Booking recommended.
Length of Visit:	3 hours for House and Gardens.
Booking Contact:	Kate Bankier Estate Office, Newby Hall, Ripon. HG4 5AE Telephone: 01423 322583 opt 3 Fax: 01423 324452
Email:	info@newbyhall.com **Website:** www.newbyhall.com
Location:	A few mins from A1between Boroughbridge and Ripon, North Yorkshire.

Please quote this guide when making a booking

These substantial walled gardens and wooded pleasure grounds are well worth visiting in all seasons: massive herbaceous borders, Victorian Kitchen garden with rare vegetable collection including new Black and White border designed by Matthew Wilson, the National Hyacinth Collection, herb and shade borders, extensive hothouses and thousands of snowdrops, bluebells, daffodils and narcissi. A stroll around the lake takes you through the deer park, where fallow deer graze beneath the boughs of living oak trees, now believed to be over a thousand years old. This walk also offers the best views of the 14th century castle. Children will have fun spotting the faces on several of our older trees.

Guided tours of the castle give you a chance to view the civil war armour, secret priests hiding hole and splendid furnishings. On site facilities include ample free parking, wc's (including disabled), tea room, historic inn with beer garden and gift shop selling plants.

Fact File

Opening Times:	Daily - Throughout the year 9am - 5pm (dusk in the winter months).
Admission Rates:	Gardens, Adults £6.00, Concession £5.50, Child £4.00. (under 5 yrs Free)
Group Rates:	Minimum group size 20 people to qualify for group rate.
	Gardens, Adults £5.50, Child £4.50.
Facilities:	Gift Shop, Plant Sales, Tea Rooms, Restaurant, Children's play area.
Disabled Access:	Yes. Toilet and parking for disabled on site. Mobility Scooter, booking necessary.
Tours/Events:	Guided tours of gardens by prior arrangement only.
Coach Parking:	Yes
Booking Contact:	Lesley Johnston-Senior
	Ripley Castle Gardens, Ripley, Nr Harrogate, North Yorkshire, HG3 3AY
	Telephone: 01423 770152 Fax: 01423 771745
Email:	enquiries@ripleycastle.co.uk
Website:	www.ripleycastle.co.uk
Location:	Three miles north of Harrogate on the A61.

Stillingfleet Lodge Garden & Nursery   Yorkshire

Walking around Stillingfleet Lodge Garden and Nurseries is a journey through one woman's passion for plants. Vanessa Cook, who is usually on hand to offer planting advice, held the National Collection of Pulmonaria and now turns her attention to trees as well as unusual perennials and climbers. She has created a charming country garden that combines cottage garden planting with traditional herbaceous borders. Abundant displays of shady planting and inspiring plant combinations with the emphasis on texture and shape, weave throughout a series of gardens creating a haven of peace. Interest continues around every corner with a wildflower meadow, wildlife pond, rare breeds of poultry and a contemporary rill garden which is a tranquil delight. Homemade cakes and refreshments are available in the converted barn. Complete your trip with a visit to the well-stocked nursery.

Fact File

Opening times: April 2nd 2011 - Sept 30th 2011, Wednesday and Friday 1.00 p.m. – 5.00 p.m.
1st and 3rd Saturdays and Sundays of each month 1.00 p.m. – 5.00 p.m.

Admission Rates: Adults: £4.00, Senior Citizens: £4.00, Children: 5 – 16 years: £0.50
RHS Members Free – on Wednesday afternoons

Group Rates: Minimum Group Size: 15
Adults: £4.00, Senior Citizens: £4.00, Children: 5 – 16 years: £0.50

Facilities: Visitor Centre, Plant Sales, Teas

Disabled Access: Yes

Toilets on site: Yes

Car Parking on site: Yes

Coach Parking: Yes – 200 yards away

Length of Visit: 1½ - 2 hours

Special Events: Courses for RHS and listed on the website.

Booking Contact: Vanessa Cook, Stillingfleet Lodge Garden and Nursery, Stewart Lane, Stillingfleet, York YO19 6HP
Booking Tel No.01904 728506. Booking Fax No. 01904 728506

Email: vanessa.cook@stillingfleetlodgenurseries.co.uk

Website: www.stillingfleetlodgenurseries.co.uk

Location: 6 miles south of York on B1222. Brown sign opposite the church.

A wonderful and romantic garden located in the vale of York, not too far from most of the stunning areas of North Yorkshire countryside.

The garden has beautiful terraces, an exotic bamboo border, Edwardian fernery and overlooks the parkland which is bordered by a Woodland Walk. In the late spring the bluebells add to the attraction and from the Woodland Walk you can enter the garden under a tunnel of yellow provided by the Laburnum Walk.

As we progress into summer old fashioned shrub roses and the herbaceous borders burst into colour. Other highlights include a fine old Ice House and magnificent specimen trees, an Austrian Pine being just one of many to note.

A visit to Sutton Park is an ideal way to relax and unwind.

Silver Award Winner 2010 in Yorkshire In Bloom.

Fact File

Opening times:	April – September: daily 11 a.m. – 5 p.m.
Admission Rates:	Adults: £3.50, Senior Citizens: £3.00, Children: £1.50
Facilities:	Shop, Plant Sales, Teas
Disabled Access:	Yes. Wheelchair loan available – booking required.
Toilets on site:	Yes
Car Parking on site:	Yes
Coach Parking:	Yes
Guided Tours:	Yes, booking required.
Length of Visit:	1 - 1.5 hours
Booking Contact:	Elaine Ellis, Sutton Park, Sutton on the Forest, York YO61 1DP Booking Tel No. 01347 810249, Booking Fax No. 01347 811251
Email:	suttonpark@statelyhome.co.uk
Website:	www.statelyhome.co.uk
Location:	8 miles north of York on B1363 in the village of Sutton on the Forest

85 acres of woodland to explore, with trees from around the world, some dating back to Medieval Times. The Arboretum has 66 Champion Trees (the largest in Britain). Spring brings fantastic displays of daffodils, lilac, cherry blossom and bluebells, which are followed by wildflowers, bring a summer picnic and relax in our picnic area or wander along one of the many trails. Autumn brings acres of spectacular colours. There are many events throughout the year, see website.

The Bird of Prey and Mammal Centre has birds from around the world. There are 3 entertaining and educational flying displays a day (with lots of audience participation!).

The Mammal Centre has lots of exciting new additions: Meerkat Island, Walk Through Wallaby Wood.

Fact File

Opening times:	Open every day except 25th & 26th December.
	Spring to Autumn 10am – 5pm, Winter 11am – 3pm
Admission Rates:	Adults £7.00, Senior Citizens £5.50, Children (4-16) £4.00
Group Rates:	Minimum Group Size 10 -Adults £5.50, Senior Citizens £5.30, Children (4-16) £3.75.
	RHS Members – Free (restricted access – see RHS handbook)
Facilities:	Licenced Tea Room, Plant Centre, Childrens Play Area,
	Dogs allowed on lead (Arboretum Only)
Disabled Access:	Yes
Toilets on Site:	Yes
Car Parking:	Yes
Coach Parking:	Yes
Wheelchair Loan:	Yes – booking required
Length of Visit:	3 - 4 hours
Special Events:	Many varied events from February to December
Booking Contact:	L McNeill
	Thorp Perrow Arboretum, Bird of Prey and Mammal Centre, Thorp Perrow,
	Bedale, North Yorkshire, DL8 2PR
	Telephone/Fax: 01677 425323
Email:	enquiries@thorpperrow.com
Website:	www.thorpperrow.com
Location:	2 miles from Bedale, 4 miles from A1

One of the most important historic gardens in the North of England, after capturing the nation's imagination on the BBC TV series 'Restoration', this hidden gem from the early 18th century has been rediscovered, restored and open to the public.

Now in the care of an independent charity, the only Grade 1 historic garden and parkland in South Yorkshire features 26 listed buildings and monuments, and is being carefully restored in a major project supported by the Heritage Lottery Fund.

Easily accessible from Leeds, Sheffield and Manchester, the painstaking restoration of the secret gardens of the Earls of Strafford has seen rare formal gardens reinstated, National Collections of Rhododendrons, Camellias and Magnolias enhanced, and over 100,000 bulbs planted throughout the 60 acre garden to create a carpet of colour. With its atmospheric views, woodland walks and majestic follies, including a dramatic viewing platform at the top of a castle folly 600 feet above sea level, there is something for everyone to enjoy in the gardens throughout the year.

Fact File

Opening Times:	Summer 10am – 5pm, Winter 10am – 4pm, Closed Christmas Day
Admission Rates:	Adults (2010) £4.75, Senior Citizens & Students (17+) £3.75, Children (5-16) £2.75 Under 5's Free, RHS Members - Free
Group Rates:	Minimum Group Size 15 – Adults £4.25, Senior Citizens & Students (17+) £3.25, Children (5-16) £2.25 Under 5's Free
Facilities:	Teas & Lunches, Visitor Information Centre
Disabled Access:	Yes
Toilets on Site:	Yes
Car/Coach Parking:	Yes
Wheelchair Loan:	Yes – Booking required. Buggies can also be booked
Length of Visit:	2 hours minimum
Special Events:	Events throughout the season. For full details visit our events section on our website. Theatre, gift fairs, Bridal fair, Car rallies, Game fair, Children's activities, Santa's Grotto
Booking Contact:	Heritage Trust Office, Wentworth Castle Gardens, Lowe Lane, Stainborough, Nr Barnsley, South Yorkshire, S75 3ET Telephone: 01226 776040 Fax: 01226 776042
Email:	heritagetrust@wentworthcastle.org **Website:** www.wentworthcastle.org
Location:	Wentworth Castle is situated in the village of Stainborough near Barnsley, about 2 miles from Junction 37 of the M1. Follow the brown signs for 'Wentworth Castle' approx 3 miles.

Please quote this guide when making a booking

The North of England's Award Winning Lavender Farm and Gardens is set in the Howardian Hills Area of Outstanding Natural Beauty, with spectacular panoramic views over the Vale of York.

The award winning gardens are a mixture of different styles including a Lavender Spiral, Mediterranean Garden, Sensory Garden and a Wildflower Meadow. In summer, the lavender with its stunning array of different colours, from white through a complete range of blues and lilacs to magnificent deep purples, along with the range of distinct and heady scents, is a wonderful experience.

Other attractions include a Specialist Plant Nursery where you will find hundreds of varieties of lavender, herbs and much more, a Deer Park, Sculpture Park and our award winning Tea Room where you can try a lavender scone which are delicious. A must!

Fact File

Opening Times:	2nd April – 30th October 2011, open daily, 10am - 5pm
Admission Rates:	Free Admission
Group Rates:	Free Admission, Free group talk (min 20), booking required
Facilities:	Visitor Centre, Plant Sales, Lavender Gift Shop, EJ's Tea Room.
Disabled Access:	Yes
Toilets on Site:	Yes
Car Parking:	Yes
Coach Parking:	Yes
Wheelchair Loan:	Yes – No Booking required
Length of Visit:	1½ - 3 hours
Special Events:	Mint festival – Sat 4th, Sun 5th June 2011, The English Lavender Festival – Sat 9th, Sun 10th July 2011. Thyme Festival – Sat 23rd, Sun 24th July 2011
Booking Contact:	Karen Young Yorkshire Lavender, Terrington, York, North Yorkshire, YO60 6PB Telephone: 01653 648008
Email:	lavenderworld@btconnect.com
Website:	www.yorkshirelavender.com
Location:	3 miles west of Castle Howard, 14 miles north east of York and 8 miles west of Malton – follow brown tourist signs.

Please quote this guide when making a booking

Samares Manor Gardens   Jersey, Channel Islands

These exceptional gardens were originally designed and constructed in the 1920s by wealthy shipping line owner, Sir James Knott. Inspired by an enthusiasm for plants and a special interest in the Orient, he created a rich diversity of planting which included many rare and special plants: a Japanese Garden, rock and water gardens, formal gardens, large ponds with islands and camellia plantations are the result of his passion.

In recent years there has been a programme of restoration, development and diversification. This included the introduction of the internationally renowned herb garden, the inspiration of designer, John Brookes. Sited in the south facing walled garden it contains hundreds of culinary, medicinal and fragrant plants; there are daily talks on their cultivation and uses. Developments over the last two years include an exotics garden, Mediterranean garden, a living willow labyrinth, and a wild flower conservation area. Amongst the native flora, the Jersey Orchid may be seen in June. Younger visitors van enjoy a junior nature hunt and "Jungle Path". The manor house and rural life museum are open by guided tour only.

Fact File

Opening Times:	9th April – 15th October 2011: 9.30 a.m. – 5 p.m.
Admission Rates:	Adults: £6.95, O.A.P: £6.50, Children over 5 / Student: £2.35.
Group Rates:	Minimum Group Size: 10
	Adults: £6.25, O.A.P: £5.75, Children over 5 / Student: £2.25.
Facilities:	Shop, plant sales, restaurant, Jersey Rural Life and Carriage Museum, Toilets.
Disabled Access:	Yes. Bookable wheelchair loan available (1 only)
Car Parking on site:	Yes
Coach Parking:	Yes
Tours/Events:	Guided tours available. Booking required.
Length of Visit:	3 hours minimum
Special Events:	Samarés Manor Country Fair 29th August 2011.
Booking Contact:	Sally Fleming, Samarès Manor, St. Clements, Jersey JE2 6QW
	Booking Telephone No. 01534 870551 Booking Fax No. 01534 768949
Email:	enquiries@samaresmanor.com
Website:	www.samaresmanor.com
Location:	From St. Helier, drive to Georgetown crossroads and follow road signs to St. Clements (A4, A5). Pass New Veterinary Hospital, bear right and turn left at traffic lights St. Clements' inner road. Pass the Roman Catholic Church on the right. Entrance to Samarès Manor is 500 yards on the left. Watch for the flags.

Scotland

'It is a golden maxim to cultivate the garden for the nose, and the eyes will take care of themselves'.

Robert Louis Stevenson

Scottish gardens are unique. Yes, they may be of similar design, or contain similar plants (not always the case) to their counterparts south of the border, but there the similarity ends. Scottish gardens are quite often immersed within the countryside, embracing far flung views beyond their borders of hills, lochs, distant mountains and the sea. The air is cool, moist and clear, which seems to make flower colour more vibrant. The soil which is quite often rich, dark and acidic helps to nourish some of the largest trees and shrubs in the British Isles and produce some of the finest spring rhododendron gardens in the temperate world. In Scottish gardens you will find plants from such far flung places as Chile, Tasmania and The Cape of Good Hope all growing happily within the same bed. From Benmore Botanic Garden in Argyll to Castle Kennedy in Dumfries and Galloway; from the Royal Botanic Garden in Edinburgh to Dunvegan Castle on the Isle of Skye, there is a whole world to discover within the gardens of Scotland.

Logan Botanic Garden - Dumfries & Galloway

Benmore with its magnificent mountainside setting is a joy to behold. Its 120 acres boast a world-famous collection of flowering trees and shrubs including over 300 species of rhododendron and over one third of the world's hardy conifer species plus fine collections from North and South America, the Orient and the Himalaya.

Visitors are welcomed by an impressive avenue of Giant Redwoods, arguably one of the finest entrances to any botanic garden in the world. Established in 1863, these majestic giants now stand over 50 metres high.

The Garden is glorious throughout the seasons, from the vibrant blooms of rhododendrons and azaleas in early spring, striking Eucryphias of late summer and breathtaking displays of rich autumn fruit and foliage.

Trails throughout the Garden lead to beautiful spots such as the restored Victorian Fernery, the Formal Garden with its distinctive Puck's Hut and hillside woodlands to a dramatic viewpoint at 450 feet (140m) overlooking the surrounding mountains and Holy Loch.

Fact File

Opening times:	Open daily from 10 a.m. 1 March – 31 October. Closing: 5 p.m. (March and October) and 6 p.m. (April – September).
Admission Rates:	Adult: 5.00, Senior Citizens: £4.00, Children: £1.00, Family: £10.00
Group Rates:	Minimum Group size: 11. For rates contact the Garden.
Facilities:	Shop, Plant Sales, Restaurant/Teas, Courtyard gallery hosting events & exhibitions, audio tours
Disabled Access:	Yes, partial
Toilets on site:	Yes
Car Parking:	Yes
Coach Parking:	Yes
Wheelchair Loan:	Yes, No Booking Required for Wheelchairs
Guided Tours:	Yes, every Tuesday/Wednesday/Thursday/Sunday at 2 p.m., no booking required
Length of Visit:	
Special Events:	Restored Victorian fernery now open.
Booking Contact:	Benmore Botanic Garden, Dunoon, Argyll PA23 8QU Booking Tel No. 01369 706261. Booking Fax No. 01369 706369
Email:	benmore@rbge.org.uk
Website:	www.rbge.org.uk/benmore
Location:	Dramatically set within the Loch Lomond and The Trossachs National Park and the Argyll Forest Park, on the A815 seven miles north of Dunoon on the Cowal Peninsula.

Please quote this guide when making a booking

North facing and steep, Bolfracks is a challenge to garden. There has been a garden here for 200 years. Owned by the same family since the 1920's, each generation has made their changes to it.

As you arrive you sweep up a long drive that in spring is just a stream of golden daffodils. An enticement to visit!

The garden is divided into a wild garden and a formal rose and herbaceous garden. The Wild garden follows a burn up, where you see marvellous spring bulbs, Hellebores, Azaleas, Rhododendrons, Meconopsis, Gunnera, Lysichiton, Primula and then wonderful autumn colours from the collection of specimem trees. We are now proud owners of a Wollemi Pine! There are wonderful views across the Tay Valley.

The formal garden has a good selection of roses, clematis, specimem trees and a new herbaceous border and peony beds. There is a wonderful Peony delavyii and a well established Prunus pissardi hedge.

Bolfracks is a garden planted with love by the current owner's uncle. Recent years have seen some much needed changes and renovation. As always, this is an ongoing process

Fact File

Opening times: April – October, Daily 10 a.m. – 6 p.m.
Admission Rates: Adults: £4.00, Child free.
Facilities: Toilet facilities, plants for sale, catering possibilities for groups.
Disabled Access: Limited
Tours: By arrangement.
Coach Parking: Yes Please call for details.
Length of Visit: 2 hours
Booking Contact: Mr & Mrs R. A. Price
Bolfracks Estate Office, Aberfeldy, Perthshire PH15 2EX
Telephone: 01887 820344, Fax: 01887 829522
Email: info@bolfracks.fsnet.co.uk
Website: www.bolfracks.com
Location: 2 miles west of Aberfeldy on A827 towards Loch Tay

Located in beautiful scenery between two large natural lochs, the Gardens extend to seventy five acres of landscaped terraces and avenues. With the romantic and ruined 16th century Castle Kennedy over looking a walled garden and a 2 acre round pond at one end, and Lochinch Castle at the other, these world famous gardens are uniquely outstanding.

In close proximity to the sea on two sides, the Gardens are greatly influenced by the Gulf Stream, and contain many fine specimens of trees, Rhododendrons and tender exotic plants. Originally designed in 1722 by the 2nd Earl of Stair, Field Marshal and Ambassador to France, who was greatly influenced by the gardens of Versailles, the gardens are full of adventure and history.

Four carefully planned walks of different lengths and interest have been designed for visitors. These reveal the full garden experience throughout the seasons including the Daffodils, Magnolias and Rhododendrons early in the year to the beautiful herbaceous borders later in the summer, as well as many woodland and loch-side walks.

Fact File

Opening Times: Weekends February, March & October, 1st April - 30th September, seven days a week, 10am- 5pm. Rest of the year by appointment.

Admission Rates: Adults £4.00, Senior Citizen £3.00, Child £1.00

Groups Rates: Minimum group size 20
10% discount on normal admission rates.

Facilities: Gift Shop, Tea room, Plant Sales

Disabled Access: Partial. Toilet and parking for disabled on site.

Tours/Events: Tours by special appointment. Annual events include an Easter Egg Hunt, Plant Fair, Family Trails as well as open-air Theatre Productions in the gardens

Coach Parking: Yes

Length of Visit: 1 - 4 hours

Booking Contact: Castle Kennedy Gardens, Stair Estates, Rephad, Stranraer, Dumfries & Galloway, DG9 8BX
Gardens Tel: 01581 400225 Telephone: 01776 702024 Fax: 01776 706248

Email: info@castlekennedygardens.co.uk

Website: www.castlekennedygardens.co.uk

Location: Approximately 3 miles east of Stranraer on A75.

Please quote this guide when making a booking

Clan Donald Skye

Clan Donald Skye Visitor Centre has a spectacular setting within the Sleat Peninsula of the Isle of Skye called the 'Garden of Skye'.

The forty acre Garden is set around the ruins of Armadale Castle. The warm, generally frost free climate of the west coast of Scotland - a result of the Gulf Stream - allows these sheltered gardens, dating back to the 17th Century, to flourish.

Wander over the expanses of lawn leading from the ruined Armadale Castle to viewpoints overlooking the hills of Knoydart. Terraced walks and landscaped ponds contrasting with wildflower meadows bring the natural and formal side by side. The Nature Trails provide another dimension to this garden experience. In May during the bluebell season, a carpet of blue around the Arboretum creates a visual and fragrance sensation that is so prevalent around the gardens at that time of year.

Fact File

Opening Times: 9.30am - 5.00pm (last entry 5pm), 7 days Thursday 4th April to Saturday 22nd October.
Admission Rates: Adults £6.95, Concessions £4.95, Child £4.95, Family £20.00.
Groups Rates: Minimum group size: 8. £4.95.
Facilities: 40 Acres of Woodland Garden and mature Trails, Museum of the Isles, Restaurant, 3 Shops.
Disabled Access: Yes, Toilet and Parking for disabled on site. Electric Wheelchairs on loan, booking necessary.
Tours/Events: Guided walks on request. Audio tour available in Museum Of The Isles - French, German, Italian, Spanish, English and Gaelic, also available, a visually impaired tour in English.
Coach Parking: Yes.
Length of Visit: 2 - 4 hours .
Booking Contact: Mags MacDonald
Armadale Castle, Armadale, Sleat, Isle of Skye, IV45 8RS
Telephone: 01471 844305 Fax: 01471 844275
Email: office@clandonald.com
Website: www.clandonald.com
Location: 2 minutes from Armadale/Mallaig Ferry. 20 miles from Skyebridge on A851.

Please quote this guide when making a booking

With over 300 years of tree planting Dawyck is truly one of the worlds finest arboreta, boasting some of the tallest trees in Britain, as well as exotic conifers and the unique Dawyck Beech. Set amidst a picturesque glen in the heart of the Scottish borders, these majestic trees form a splendid backdrop to the abundance of native and exotic plants on display.

The Garden is a magical place throughout the year, from swathes of snowdrops and daffodils in early spring to breathtaking displays of azaleas, rhododendrons and pools of blue Himalayan poppies in early summer.

In autumn the foliage bursts into vivid hues of red, orange and gold and provides a magnificent backdrop of colour.

Dawyck's award winning state-of-the-art visitor centre greatly enhances the visitor experience at this renowned botanic garden.

Fact File

Opening times:	Open daily from 10 a.m. 1 February – 30 November. Closes 4 p.m. February & November; 5 p.m. March & October; 6 p.m. April – September.
Admission Rates:	Adults: £5.00, Senior Citizens: £4.00, Children: £1.00
Group Rates:	Minimum Group Size 10. Adults: £4.50, Senior Citizens: £3.60, Children: £0.90
Facilities:	Visitor Centre, Shop, Plant sales, Cafe, studio for exhibitions and events
Disabled Access:	Yes.
Toilets on site:	Yes.
Car Parking on site:	Yes.
Coach Parking:	Yes.
Booking Contact:	Vicky Brunt, Dawyck Botanic Garden, Stobo, Near Peebles, Scottish Borders, EH45 9JU Booking Tel No.01721 760254 Booking Fax No. 01721 760214
Email:	dawyck@rbge.org.uk
Website:	www.rbge.org.uk/dawyck
Location:	28 miles south of Edinburgh on the B712, 8 miles southwest of Peebles in the Scottish Borders.

Hidden away in Galloway, Dunskey Gardens & Maze are an undiscovered delight. From the swathes of snowdrops in late winter through the tapestry of flowers of summer and the warm glowing colours of autumn, there is always something to see in these relaxed and welcoming gardens.

Plant enthusiasts will be fascinated by the wide range of flora, including the National Collection of Clianthus and Sutherlandia, whilst other visitors simply choose a favourite bench and enjoy the tranquillity.

The more energetic can explore the Woodland Gardens, the Maze or try some of the children's simple activities such as the Tree Spotting Game. Dunskey is also home to the popular Seasons Tearoom which prides itself on the quality of its light lunches and good home baking. Dunskey is situated close to the pretty harbour village of Portpatrick, making an ideal destination for a weekend break.

Fact File

Opening times: February and March week-ends only.   April - October Daily 10a.m. - 5p.m.
Other times by arrangement including evening visits.

Admission Rates: Adults £4.30. Senior Citizens £4.00. Children under 16 £2.00

Group Rates: Minimum 15 - 10% discount.

Facilities: Tearoom with murals and an open air terrace. Shop. Plant sales. Shaded dog parking.

Disabled Access: Tearoom and mobility scooter available for garden, free. Toilet and parking.

Events: Guided tour with gardener every Wednesday 11.30a.m. Wedding photographs. See website.

Tours: Yes. Booking advisable. House opened for tours by arrangement.

Coach Parking: Yes.

Car Parking: Yes.

Length of visit: 1-2 hrs.

Booking Contact: Dunskey Gardens, Portpatrick, Stranraer, Dumfries and Galloway DG9 8TJ
Telephone 01776 810905   Fax 01776 810 581

E-mail: garden@dunskey.com

Website: www.dunskey.com

Location: Brown signs. 1 ml from Portpatrick, 8 mls from Stranraer off B738

Dunvegan Castle Gardens
Isle of Skye

Any visit to the Isle of Skye is incomplete without savouring the wealth of history offered by Dunvegan Castle & Gardens, the oldest continuously inhabited castle in Scotland and ancestral home of the Chiefs of clan MacLeod for 800 years.

Dunvegan Castle's five acres of formal gardens began life in the 18th century. In stark contrast to the barren moorland and mountains that dominate Skye's landscape, the gardens are a hidden oasis featuring an eclectic mix of plants, woodland glades, shimmering pools fed by waterfalls and streams flowing down to the sea. After experiencing the Water Garden with its ornate bridges and islands replete with a rich and colourful plant variety, wander through the elegant surroundings of the formal Round Garden featuring a Box-wood Parterre as its centrepiece

For more information about our opening times and our Friends of Dunvegan Castle membership scheme, please visit www.dunvegancastle.com

Fact File

Opening times:	1 April – 15 October 10 a.m. – 5.30 p.m. 16 October – 31 March: open by appointment
Admission Rates:	Castle & Gardens: Adults: £9.00, Senior Citizens/Students: £7.00, Family (2 Adults, 3 Children) £24.00, Children (5-15 yrs): £4.50, Cruise Ships using pontoon facilities £9.50 Gardens Only: Adult: £7.00, Senior Citizens/Students: £6.00, Children (5-15 yrs): £3.50
Group Rates:	Minimum Group Size: 10. Castle & Gardens £7.00, Gardens Only £6.00
Facilities:	Shop, Café, seal boat trips, fishing and loch cruises, Dunvegan Castle
Disabled Access:	Yes.
Toilets on site:	Yes
Car Parking on site:	Yes
Coach Parking:	Yes
Booking Contact:	Macleod Estate Office, Dunvegan Castle & Gardens, Dunvegan, Isle of Skye, Scotland, IV55 8WF Booking Tel No.01470 521206. Booking Fax No. 01470 521205
Email:	info@dunvegancastle.com
Website:	www.dunvegancastle.com
Location:	1 mile north of Dunvegan on the northwest corner of Skye.

Please quote this guide when making a booking

Glenwhan Gardens Scotland

In May 2010 Tessa and Bill Knott celebrated thirty years of building their Dumfries and Galloway garden of Glenwhan. Beautiful, calm and unusual it always impresses even the most hardy of garden creators and horticulturalists. Created from a rough windswept hillside, with thin soil over rocks laid bare by upland farming and westerly gales, the feat is astounding. Twelve acres of still expanding paths and planting continue into the moorland above. A burn flows down from the moor to two large man-made ponds and the lush planting below. Navigating through the winding flowery ways give a sense of exploration, and arrival at the higher viewpoints provide moments of peaceful contemplation as the wide expanse of Luce Bay is revealed before you.
In this setting, on a sunny day with blue sea and sky, Tessa celebrated the thirty years of her garden with her family and friends and what a special day it was too!

Fact File

Opening Times:	April – October 30th, 10am – 5pm
Admission Rates:	Adults £5.00, Senior Citizens £4.00, Children and students £2.00
Group Rates:	Group Rates £4.00, add £1.00 per person for guided tour. Please book ahead for group bookings
Facilities:	Visitor Centre, tea room, plant sales
Disabled Access:	Yes
Toilets on Site:	Yes
Car Parking:	Yes
Coach Parking:	Yes
Wheelchair Loan:	Yes
Length of Visit:	2 hours
Booking Contact:	Tessa Knott Glenwhan Gardens, Dunragit, Nr Stranraer, Wigtownshire, DG9 8PH Telephone: 01581 400222
Email:	tess@glenwhan.freeserve.co.uk
Website:	www.glenwhangardens.co.uk
Location:	Refer to website

Please quote this guide when making a booking

This exotic Garden, justifiably described as a plantsman's paradise, is home to a spectacular collection of bizarre and beautiful plants. This majestic corner of Scotland is warmed by the Gulf Stream and the climate provides perfect growing conditions for southern hemisphere plants.

Famed for its tender collections, Logan's Walled Garden is a showcase for colourful blooms throughout the season. Adding to the summer colour are Osteospermums, gazanias and diascias – all half-hardy perennials from southern Africa. The Woodland Garden is a haven for the weird and wonderful, from the groves of eucalyptus to the Gunnera Bog and the evocative Tasmanian Creek planting. Visitors who venture to the highest point of the Garden will be rewarded with magnificent views over the Rhins to the Galloway Hills and beyond.

Over 1,800 different plant species, including around 120 that are threatened in the wild, can be seen thriving within Logan's 24-acre site.

Fact File

Opening times:	Open daily from 10 a.m. 15th March - 31st October. (Sundays only in February 4 p.m.) March & October 5 p.m. April - September 6 p.m. (Sundays only in February), 5 p.m. March & October; 6 p.m. April – September
Admission Rates:	Adults: £5.00, Concessions: £4.00, Children: £1.00, Family £10.00
Group Rates:	Minimum Group Size: 11, 10% discount.
Facilities:	Visitor Centre, Shop, Plant Sales, Potting Shed Bistro, Teas, Audio guides
Disabled Access:	Yes
Toilets on site:	Yes
Car Parking on site:	Yes
Coach Parking:	Yes
Guided Tours:	Yes, 10.30a.m. every second Tuesday of the month (April – September) pre-booked tours available.
Booking Contact:	Richard Baines, Logan Botanic Gardens, Port Logan, Stranraer, Dumfries & Galloway DG9 9ND Booking Tel No.01776 860231. Booking Fax No. 01776 860333
Email:	logan@rbge.org.uk
Website:	www.rbge.org.uk/logan
Location:	14 miles south of Stranraer in the Rhins of Galloway, off the B7065.

Please quote this guide when making a booking

Established in 1670, the Royal Botanic Garden Edinburgh has developed into a world leading centre of horticultural excellence and its 70 magnificent acres are home to seven per cent of all known plants.

At the heart of the Garden stands the iconic Palm House - the tallest of its kind in Britain. Within the Glasshouses you will enjoy a fascinating journey through the tropical and temperate regions of the globe as you wander through ten distinct climatic zones.

Reflecting the international research and conservation work of RBGE, the Garden is home to the largest collection of wild-origin Chinese plants outside China. See, too, the Scottish Heath Garden, recreating the plantings and landscape of the Scottish highlands; the world-famous Rock Garden; the stunning 165-long Herbaceous Border, backed by an outstanding century-old Beech Hedge and don't miss the Queen Mother's Memorial Garden – an inspirational tribute to a much-loved royal.

Fact File

Opening times:	Open daily from 10am (except 25th December and 1st January), closing 6pm February - October and closing 4pm in November, December and January.
Admission Rates:	Adults: Free, Senior Citizens: Free, Children: Free. A charge applies to the glasshouses
Disabled Access:	Yes. Wheelchair loan available – booking required.
Toilets on site:	Yes
Car Parking on site:	On street, metered Mon-Fri. Weekend free.
Coach Parking:	On street, metered Mon-Fri. Weekend free.
Guided Tours:	Yes, to book guided tours please contact the Garden Rangers Team.
Length of Visit:	Guided tours depart daily at 11 a.m. & 2 p.m., April – September. Booked tours for groups available throughout the year
Special Events:	The John Hope Gateway Biodiversity and Information Centre now open
Booking Contact:	To book guided tours, please contact Garden Rangers Team. Booking Tel No.0131 248 2909. Booking Fax No. 0131 248 2901
Email:	gardentours@rbge.org.uk
Website:	www.rbge.org.uk/the-gardens/edinburgh/guided-tours
Location:	One mile north of Princes Street on the A092, with entrances on Arboretum Place, Inverleith Row.

Please quote this guide when making a booking

Wales

Ireland

'It was for the garden's sake (Brondanw) that I worked and stinted, for its sake that I chiefly hoped to prosper. A cheque for ten pounds would come in and I would order yew hedging to that extent, a cheque for twenty and I would pave a further piece of terrace.'

Clough Williams-Ellis

There are some magical gardens to be found in Wales, ranging from iconic modern-day creations such as the remarkable National Botanic Garden of Wales to superb garden restorations such as at Aberglasney Gardens in Carmarthenshire, where there is a fully restored Elizabethan Cloister Garden. For me however, one of the delights of Wales is that there are so many hidden garden gems, tucked away within the folds of hill and mountain. In the pages that follow you will discover some of these gems. Why not make 2011 the year you visit them?

'You will never plough a field, or dig a patch, by turning it over in your mind'.

Anon - Irish proverb

The weather is soft in Ireland, seldom offering extremes of heat or cold, just copious gifts of gently falling rain and mild airstreams enabling every landscape, plant and garden to green and grow. Irish gardens are like no other; they too are soft and gentle, full of atmosphere and a fecundity of foliage. The following pages provide just a little taster of some of the finest Irish gardens including Cashel House and Benvarden.

National Botanic Garden Of Wales - Carmarthenshire

Cashel House Hotel & Gardens - Co Galway

Aberglasney Gardens Carmarthenshire

Aberglasney is one of the finest gardens in Wales. The Gardens have wonderful horticultural qualities and a mysterious history. Within the ten acres of garden are six different garden spaces including three walled gardens. At its heart is a unique and fully restored Elizabethan /Jacobean Cloister Garden and a parapet walk, which is the only example that survived in the UK. The Garden contains a magnificent collection of rare and unusual plants which are seldom seen elsewhere in the country.

The Mansion and Garden will continually be improved over the years, the result is a world renowned Garden set in the beautiful landscape of the Tywi Valley. There is a Café in the grounds, which serves delectable light lunches and snacks. In the summer, tea can be taken on the terrace overlooking the Pool Garden. There is also a shop and plant sales area. The creation of a winter garden in 2005 called the Ninfarium (after the mediaeval garden near Rome) is situated in the ruinous central courtyard of the Mansion. It provides a unique garden environment, displaying a wonderful range of exotic sub-tropical plants.

Fact File

Opening times:	Summer: 10am - 6pm (last entry at 5pm).
	Winter: 10.30am - 4pm (last entry at 3pm).
Admission Rates:	Adult/OAP £7.00, Child £4.00, Family £18.00.
Groups Rates:	Groups 10+
	Adult/OAP £6.00.
Facilities:	Shop, Plant Sales, Cafe.
Disabled Access:	Yes. Toilet and parking for disabled on site. Wheelchairs on loan, booking necessary.
Tours/Events:	Guided tours on request.
Coach Parking:	Yes
Length of Visit:	2 - 4 hours
Booking Contact:	Bookings Department.
	Aberglasney Gardens, Llangathen, Carmarthenshire, SA32 8QH
	Telephone: 01558 668998 Fax: 01558 668998
Email:	info@aberglasney.org
Website:	www.aberglasney.org
Location:	Four miles outside Llandeilo off the A40.

Bodnant Garden is one of the finest gardens in the country not only known for its magnificent collections of rhododendrons, camellias and magnolias but also for its idyllic setting above the River Conwy with extensive views of the Snowdonia range.

Visit in early Spring (March and April) and be rewarded by the sight of carpets of golden daffodils and other spring bulbs, as well as the beautiful blooms of the magnolias, camellias and flowering cherries. The spectacular rhododendrons and azaleas will delight from mid April until late May, whilst the famous original Laburnum Arch is an overwhelming mass of yellow blooms from mid-may to mid-June. The herbaceous borders, roses, hydrangeos, clematis and water liles flower from the middle of June until September.

All these, together with the outstanding October autumn colours make Bodnant truly a garden offering interest for all the seasons.

Fact File

Opening Times:	26th Feb-31st Oct 10-5pm. 1st Nov-13th Nov 10-4pm. Last entry 30mins prior to closing.
Admission Rates:	Adults £8.50, Child £4.25 (5-16yrs)
Groups Rates:	Minimum group size 15.
	Adults £7.40.
Facilities:	Tearoom, Car & Coach Park. Garden Centre, Art & Craft Studios (Not NT).
Disabled Access:	Yes accessible toilet and parking on site. Wheelchairs on loan.
Tours/Events:	Phone for details
Coach Parking:	Yes
Length of Visit:	2 hours +
Booking Contact:	Ann Smith
	Bodnant Garden, Tal Y cafn, Nr Colwyn Bay, Conwy. LL28 5RE
	Telephone: 01492 650460 Fax: 01492 650448
Email:	ann.smith@nationaltrust.org.uk
Website:	www.bodnant-garden.co.uk
Location:	8 miles south of Llandudno and Colwyn Bay just off A470, signposted from the A55, exit at junction 19.

Please quote this guide when making a booking

Established since 1989, Cae Hir Gardens were entirely envisaged, designed and created by just one man, Dutchman Wil Akkermans. Over the past 20 years his labour of love has matured into one of Wales' most acclaimed gardens, being featured in both of 2009's prestigious "The Gardens of Wales" and "Discovering Welsh Gardens" books. In 2004 Cae Hir also proudly accepted an invitation by the RHS to become a partner garden. This acclaim comes as a result of Wil's creativity and originality in his pioneering approach to blending the wild with the cultivated.

- "What a truly magnificent garden … so beautifully landscaped. I have not seen a garden quite like it anywhere." *Gordon and Ivy Morris, July 2009.*
- "Eat your heart out Monty Don." *Joe Frostman, June 2009.*
- "Delicious cream tea, a wonderfully relaxing garden, nice people – what more could you ask of a Sunday afternoon!" *Liz, Austria, July 2009.*

Fact File

Opening Times:	Easter to October, daily from 10 a.m. – 5 p.m.
Admission Rates:	Adults: £5.00, Senior Citizens: £5.00, Children: £1.00
Group Rates:	Minimum Group Size: 10-24 or 25+, Adults: £4.50 or £4.00, Senior Citizens: £4.50 or £4.00 Children: N/A.
Facilities:	Shop, plant sales, tearoom
Disabled Access:	Yes, partial
Toilets:	Yes.
Tours/Events:	See website
Car Parking:	Yes.
Coach Parking:	Yes.
Length of Visit:	2-3 hours
Booking Contact:	Julie Akkermans Cae Hir Gardens, Cribyn, Lampeter, Ceredigion SA48 7NG Telephone. 01570 471116
Email:	caehirgardens@gmail.com
Website:	www.caehirgardens.com
Location:	West from Lampeter or east from Aberaeron on the A482. In Temple Bar turn onto the B4337 towards Llanybydder. The gardens are two miles down the road in Cribyn (left-hand side).

Please quote this guide when making a booking

THE secret is out . . . Dewstow's Hidden Gardens and Grottoes are rapidly becoming one of the most fascinating tourist attractions in South Wales. Situated just a few miles from the M4 motorway and the two Severn Bridges, the Dewstow estate offers a magical oasis of calm, set in the magnificent Monmouthshire countryside.

The "lost" gardens, which date back to the late 1890s, became buried by tons of soil around the time of the Second World War but were rediscovered by new owners in 2000. Now, due to a painstaking and meticulous renovation programme, Dewstow's buried treasure has been unveiled once again and is being viewed and enjoyed by a long line of enchanted visitors.

Dewstow, now Grade One listed, features a stunning series of gardens, pools, water features and ornamental areas just waiting to be explored at your leisure. Don't miss the chance to take a fascinating journey back in time in this subterranean wonderland before relaxing with some refreshments in our delightful tea room.

Fact File

Opening Times: Daily from Saturday March 19th until Sunday 30th October 2011. 10.00am – 4.30p.m.
Admission Rates: Adults: £6.50, Senior Citizens: £5.50, Children (11-18): £4.00, under 10's FREE.
Group Rates: Minimum Group Size 10, Adults: £5.50, Senior Citizens: £5.50, Children: £3.50.
Facilities: Plant sales, teas.
Disabled Access: Very limited in the gardens.
Toilets on site: Yes.
Coach Parking: Yes.
Car Parking on site: Yes.
Length of Visit: 2 hours approximately.
Booking Contact: Liz, Dewstow Gardens, Caerwent, Monmouthshire NP26 5AH
Telephone: 01291 430444
Fax: 01291 425816
Email: gardens@dewstow.co.uk
Website: www.dewstow.co.uk/gardens.htm

Please quote this guide when making a booking

The Dingle garden is set in the heart of glorious mid-Wales. The four acre garden is mostly the work of Barbara Joseph who over the years, created a secluded and beautiful area which serves to inspire garden lovers everywhere.

The R.H.S. partner garden is south-facing with paths that wind down the slope to a lake and small waterfall. The beds are colour themed to look good all year round. Spectacular autumn foliage, including many unusual trees, shrubs and acers, along with an acre primrose and bluebell wood are special features. This peaceful haven, teeming with wildlife is the ideal spot for a relaxing wander at any time of year.

The Dingle Nursery runs alongside the garden and offers for sale a huge variety of common and rare plants and trees, many of which grow there.

Fact File

Opening Times:	9 – 5 every day. Only closed for one week at Christmas
Admission Rates:	Adults: £3.50, Senior Citizens: £3.50, Children: Free, R.H.S. members free.
Group Rates:	No reduction for groups (free tea and coffee included in the price)
Facilities:	Small shop with free tea and coffee available.
Disabled Access:	Very limited. 1 wheelchair available for booking. Car Parking and toilet on site.
Tours/Events:	No guided tours. Talk for groups.
Coach Parking:	Yes.
Length of Visit:	1 – 3 hours.
Booking Contact:	Jill Rock, The Dingle Garden, Frochas, Nr. Welshpool, Powys. SY21 9JD Tel: 01938 555145 Fax: 01938 555778
Email:	info@dinglenurseryandgarden.co.uk
Website:	www.dinglenurseryandgarden.co.uk
Location:	2 miles north of Welshpool, off the A490.

Please quote this guide when making a booking

Set in the heart of the Vale of Glamorgan countryside, Dyffryn is one of Wales' largest and most important Edwardian Gardens. The impressive 55 acres are a result of the unique collaboration of landscape architect Thomas Mawson and avid plant collector Reginald Cory.

Dyffryn boasts a magnificent double herbaceous border, a Victorian fernery, a rose garden, a stumpery, a rockery and also an extensive tree collection in the arboretum. As you stroll the beautiful grounds you will also discover a series of intimate garden rooms, such as the Pompeian Garden, Lavender Court and the Reflecting pool.

This outstanding garden has been undergoing considerable restoration works with assistance from the Heritage Lottery Fund. The extensive project is due to conclude this year with the exciting revival of the walled garden and the reinstatement of the magnificent glasshouses.

Fact File

Opening Times: Site open throughout the year. 1st March – 31st October 10am – 6pm.
1st November – 28th February 10am - 4pm.

Admission Rate: 1st March – 31st October Adults £6.50, Concession £4.50, Child £2.50, Family £17.00.
1st November – 29th February Adult £3.50, Concession £2.50, Child £1.50, Family £8.50.

Group Rates: Discount on groups of 15 and over, please contact for more details.

Facilities: Visitor centre, Tearooms, Play area and plant sales all before the pay barrier

Disabled Access: Majority of gardens is wheelchair friendly.
Wheelchairs available to loan, advanced booking is preferable.

Tours/Events: Tours available to groups by prior arrangement at an additional charge. Tours with Head Gardener held throughout the year, please contact for more details.
Varied programme of seasonal events and activities held throughout the year.

Coach Parking: Yes

Length of Visit: 2 – 3 hours

Booking Contact: Dyffryn Gardens, St Nicholas, Vale of Glamorgan, CF5 6SU.
Tel: 029 2059 3328, Fax: 029 2059 1966

Email: dyffryn@valeofglamorgan.gov.uk

Website: www.dyffryngardens.com

Location: Exit M4 at J33 to A4232(signposted Barry). At roundabout take 1st exit (A4232). At junction with A48/A4050 exit the A4232 at Culverhouse Cross Take 4th exit A48 (signposted Cowbridge). Turn left at lights in St Nicholas.
Dyffryn is on right after approx. 1½ miles.

Glansevern Hall Gardens Powys

Glansevern Hall was built, in Greek Revival style, by Sir Arthur Davies Owen at the turn of the 18th/19th Century.

It looks down on the River Severn from an enclosure of gardens (25 acres) set in wider parkland. Near the house are fine lawns studded with herbaceous and rose beds and a wide border backed by brick walls. A Victorian orangery and a large fountain face each other across the lawns. The large walled garden has been ingeniously divided into compartments separated by hornbeam hedges and ornamental ironwork. There is a rock garden of exceptional size, built of limestone and tufa, which creates a walk-through grotto. A little further afield, woodland walks are laid out around the 4 acre lake and pass through a water garden which, especially in May and June, presents a riot of growth and colour. One walk leads to a bird hide on the banks of the Severn.

Glansevern is noted for its collection of unusual trees.

Dogs are welcome on a lead.

Fact File

Opening times:	May to September every Thursday, Friday, Saturday and Bank Holiday Monday 12.00 noon - 5.00 pm Groups on any other day, booking necessary.
Admission Rates:	Adult £6.00, Seniors £5.50, Children under sixteen Free.
Facilities:	Tea Room & Light Lunches (all Homemade), Shop
Disabled Access:	Yes. Toilet and parking for disabled on site.
Tours/Events:	Guided walk indentifying the large number of unusual trees.
Coach Parking:	Yes
Length of Visit:	1 ½ hours
Booking Contact:	Neville Thomas Glansevern Hall Gardens, Berriew, Welshpool, Powys, SY21 8AH Telephone: 01686 640644
Email:	glansevern@yahoo.co.uk
Website:	www.glansevern.co.uk
Location:	Signposted at Berriew on A483 between Welshpool and Newtown, North Powys, 4 miles S W of Powis Castle.

The remarkable National Botanic Garden of Wales is a very special place. The largest single-span Glasshouse in the world designed by Norman Foster, poised in the landscape like a giant raindrop is home to some of the most endangered plants on the planet from six Mediterranean climate regions, Western Australia, Chile, the Canaries, California, southern Africa and the Mediterranean basin. It helps protect and conserve what is considered to be the best collection of its kind in the world. The Tropical House located in the unique and historic double-walled garden is bursting with palms, pineapples, coconuts, cardamom and scores of orchids. The Garden lies on land that was once a magnificent Regency water park, many of the original features having been restored. Discover lakes, ponds, walks; theatre; licensed restaurant; shop; gallery; bog garden, apiary; Physicians of Myddfai Exhibition and Apothecaries' Garden; children's play area and discovery centre. Land surrounding the Garden has been designated a National Nature Reserve.

Fact File

Opening times: 10 a.m. – 6 p.m. BST/10 a.m. – 4.30 p.m. BWT. (Closed Christmas Day)

Admission Rates: Adults: £8.50, Senior Citizens: £7.00, Children: Under 16: £4.50, Under 5s: Free
Family: 2 Adults + 4 Children £21.00

Group Rates: Minimum Group Size: 10. Adults: £7.50, Senior Citizens: £6.00, Children: £3.50
RHS members free – between 1st October and 31st March.

Facilities: Shop, Plant Sales, Licensed Restaurant, Café, 360 degree Multimedia Theatre, Conference Centre, Children's Playground, Activity Centre.

Disabled Access: Yes. Wheelchair loan available, Motorised wheelchair £3 per day, manual wheelchairs free (booking advisable).

Toilets on site: Yes

Car Parking on site: Yes

Coach Parking: Yes

Guided Tours: Yes, booking required.

Length of Visit: 4-6 hours

Special Events: Full events programme

Booking Contact: National Botanic Garden of Wales, Llanarthne, Carmarthenshire, SA32 8HG
Booking Tel No. 01558 668768. Booking Fax No. 01558 668933

Email: info@gardenofwales.org.uk

Website: www.gardenofwales.org.uk

Location: One hour's drive from Cardiff, two hours from Bristol.
Just off the A48 which links directly to the M4 and on to the M5.

Please quote this guide when making a booking

Picton Castle Gardens & Gallery Pembrokeshire

Soak up a special magic as you walk beneath some of the largest and oldest trees in West Wales. The 40 acres of walled and woodland gardens around Picton Castle include a tree fern glade, a restored dew pond and the new jungle garden planted with gingers, banana trees and other vibrant exotics. Unique to Picton are Rhododendrons bred here, plus rare species like Embothrium, Eucryphia and an avenue of myrtles.

Massive Redwoods and oaks dominate the Avenues. Around them, rare trees and flowering shrubs include the largest Rhododendron 'Old Port' in existence, a particularly fine Dawn Redwood (a conifer presumed extinct until rediscovered in remote Chinese valley in 1941) and numerous rare conifers from all over the globe.

Scent and colour rule the Walled Garden, where a vast collection of border plants create riotous summer colour. Equally tantalising is Maria's Mediterranean Restaurant, in the Victorian courtyard.

Fact File

Opening times:	28th March to 30th September daily 10.30am – 5.00pm. Entrance to the Castle by guided tour only. Check website for dates and times of February and October half term opening and occasional winter weekend openings.
Admission Rates:	Gardens & Gallery: Adults £5.00, Senior Citizens £4.75, Children 5 – 15: £2.50 With Castle tour Adults £7.50, Seniors £7.25, Children £4.00
Group Rates:	Reductions on Castle tours for pre-booked groups of 20 or more. RHS Members Free from April – September
Facilities:	Shop, plant sales, restaurant, teas, art galleries, castle tours, children's play area, picnic area, toilets.
Disabled Access:	Yes. Free wheelchair loan available.
Car Parking on site:	Yes
Coach Parking:	Yes
Tours/Events:	Guided tours to Castle only. Booking only required for large groups on Castle tours
Length of Visit:	2 hours for castle tour and Walled Garden, plus 2 hours for 40 acres of woodland gardens.
Special Events:	See website for information.
Booking Contact:	Dai Evans Picton Castle Gardens & Gallery, Picton Castle, Haverfordwest, Pembrokeshire SA62 4AS Telephone & Fax No. 01437 751326.
Email:	info@pictoncastle.co.uk Website www.pictoncaste.co.uk
Location:	OS Ref: SN011 135; two miles south of the A40. Follow brown tourist signs located on the A40 about 3 miles east of Haverfordwest,

Set in the heart of the Snowdonia National Park; Plas Tan y Bwlch is a 13 acre picturesque Victorian garden situated in the Vale of Ffestiniog and overlooking the small village of Maentwrog.

Predominantly a woodland garden; the gardens host a large variety Rhododendrons and Azaleas mixed with planting of both native and exotic plants and maintained using wildlife friendly practices. There is also a large ornamental pond, a sensory garden and a Rhododendron tunnel all of which are overlooked by a large Victorian mansion that is currently run as a study centre by the Snowdonia National Park.

Fact File

Opening Times:	Throughout the year 10.00am till dusk. Conservatory 10am – 4pm. House varies.
Admission Rates:	Admission to the Garden, free of charge but donations welcome.
Group Rates:	Please phone for details
Facilities:	Teas. Public and professional courses available refer to website for details.
Disabled Access:	Yes
Toilets on Site:	Yes
Coach Parking:	Yes
Length of Visit:	1 - 2 hours
Special Events:	Volunteer days refer to website for details
Booking Contact:	Plas Tan-Y-Bwlch, Maentwrog, Blaenau ffestiniog, Gwynedd, LL41 3YU Telephone: 01766 772600 Fax: 01766 772609
Website:	www.plastanybwlch
Location:	Plas Tan y Bwlch is located approximately 6 miles east of the coastal town of Porthmadog on the A487

The eighteenth-century house is set on wide open lawns leading down to the Bush River crossed by a fine Victorian iron bridge some 36 metres long. A walk through the surrounding parkland leads to a pond surrounded by azaleas, magnolias, rhododendrons, Japanese maples and Irish yews and a lushness of gunneras, irises, darmeras and other moisture-loving plants. The walled garden, where brick-faced walls are lined with espaliered apple and pear trees and a formal rose garden centred on a small pool and fountain is flanked on one side by a formal box parterre, provides a touch of old-world elegance. On the other side of the fountain a framework was constructed to give support to a mixture of climbers – wisteria, clematis etc, a variety of ivies and the pink and cream-splashed Actinidia kolomikta, while the gravel paths are lined with old cottage garden favourites like lupins, peonies and roses, punctuated by clipped cones and pyramids of yew and box. An open arch in the walls leads through to a one-acre kitchen garden abundant with fruit trees, vegetables and herbs, all contained within immaculately maintained box hedges. There is also a small plant sales area.

Fact File

Opening Times:	12 – 5 p.m. from 1st June – 30th August. Open in May by arrangement.
Admission Rates:	Adults: £4.00, Senior Citizens: £4.00, Children: free under 14
Group Rates:	Minimum Group Size: 10. Adults: £3.00, Senior Citizens:, Children: free under 14 RHS Members 2 for 1.
Facilities:	Plant Sales, Teas, small museum of old farm implements etc.
Disabled Access:	Yes.
Toilet On Site:	Yes.
Tours:	Yes. Booking required. House opened for groups by arrangement.
Coach Parking:	Yes.
Car Parking:	Yes.
Length of Visit:	1-2 hours
Booking Contact:	Benvarden, 36 Benvarden Road, Ballybogey, Co. Antrim, BT53 6NN. Tel. 028 20741331 Fax. 028 20741955
Email:	mail@benvarden.com
Website:	www.benvarden.com
Location:	On B67 Coleraine Ballycastle road. Brown tourist signs. 10 miles from Giants Causeway and Bushmills..

Please quote this guide when making a booking

Cashel house is a gracious country house owned by the McEvilly family. The gardens are an informal country house style based on a number of woodland glades. The garden contains profusion of roses both old fashioned and modern along with many herbaceous plants with naturalised day lilies, astilbes and primulas. Also camellias, magnolias, azaleas, eucryphia and many more. Our own herb and fruit gardens, stud farm and garden school are also on site.

Fact File

Opening times:	10.30 – 5 p.m. each day from 12 February – 1 December.
Admission Rates:	Adults: £5.00, Senior Citizens: £3.00, Children and students: £3.00 RHS members free
Group Rates:	Minimum Group Size: Adults: 40/50, Senior Citizens: 30/40, Children: 8/10
Facilities:	Plant Sales, Restaurant, Teas, Garden, Courses
Disabled Access:	Part of the garden, all of the house, booking required for wheelchairs
Toilets on site:	Yes
Car Parking on site:	Yes
Coach Parking:	Yes, for small coaches 20 – 60 persons
Guided Tours:	Yes, booking required
Special Events:	Garden courses, 2 or 3 days or one day, see leaflet attached
Booking Contact:	Kay McEvilly, Cashel House Hotel & Gardens, Cashel, Connamara, Co. Galway Booking Tel No.353 95 31001. Booking Fax No. 353 95 81077
Email:	res@cashel-house-hotel.com
Website:	www.cashel-house-hotel.com
Location:	West coast of Ireland, 40 miles from Galway, 8 from Roundstone, 8 from Carna, 12 from Clifden

Please quote this guide when making a booking

Index

Abbey House Gardens	134	Cothay Manor & Gardens	110
Abbotsbury Subtropical Gardens	42	Coton Manor	97
Aberglasney Gardens	167	Cotswold Farm Garden	53
Anglesey Abbey, Gardens & Lode Mill	13	Cotswold Wildlife Park & Gardens	102
Arley Arboretum	140	Cottesbrooke Hall & Gardens	98
Arley Hall & Gardens	19		
Arundel Castle	126	Dawyck Botanic Garden	160
		Deene Park	99
Batsford Arboretum & Wild Garden	50	Dewstow Gardens & Grottoes	170
Belvoir Castle	83	Dingle Garden (The)	171
Benmore Botanic Garden	156	Dorothy Clive Garden (The)	114
Bennetts Water Gardens	43	Dunskey Gardens	161
Benvarden	177	Dunvegan Castle Gardens	162
Berkeley Castle	49	Dyffryn Gardens	172
Birmingham Botanical Gardens & Glasshouses	89		
Blenheim Palace	100	East Lambrook	111
Bodnant Garden	168	Elgood's Brewery Gardens	15
Bolfracks	157	Elton Hall Gardens	16
Borde Hill Garden, Park & Woodland	127	Enys Gardens	27
Boughton House	95	Exbury Gardens & Steam Railway	65
Bourton House Gardens	52		
Bowood Rhododendron Woodland Garden	135	Forde Abbey & Gardens	44
Brantwood	32	Fountains Abbey & Studley Royal Water Garden	144
Breezy Knees Garden	142		
Broomhill Sculpture Gardens	36	Garden at the Bannut (The)	68
Burncoose Nurseries	25	Garden House (The)	38
Burton Agnes Hall & Gardens	143	Glansevern Hall Gardens	173
Buscot Park	101	Glenwhan Gardens	163
		Gooderstone Water Gardens	90
Cadlands	64	Great Chalfield Manor & Gardens	136
Cae Hir	169	Great Comp Garden	73
Caerhays Castle Garden	26	Great Dixter House & Gardens	120
Cambridge Botanic Garden	14	Green Island Gardens	47
Cannington (Walled Garden of)	108	Groombridge Place Gardens & Enchanted Forest	74
Capel Manor Gardens	86		
Cashel House Hotel & Gardens	178	Hall Place & Gardens	75
Castle Ashby Gardens	96	Ham House	115
Castle Hill	37	Hampton Court Castle & Gardens	69
Castle Kennedy & Gardens	158	Harlow Carr - RHS Garden	145
Chalice Well	109	Hartland Abbey	39
Chelsea Physic Garden	85	Helmsley Walled Garden	146
Chenies Manor House	10	Herstmonceux Castle - Garden & Grounds	121
Cheshire Gardens of Distinction	18	Hestercombe Gardens	112
Cholmondeley	20	Hever Castle & Gardens	76
Clan Donald Skye	159	Hidcote Manor Garden	54
Cliveden	11	High Beeches Gardens	128
Consall Hall Gardens	113	Hodnet Hall	106

Index

Hole Park Gardens	77
Hoveton Hall Gardens	91
Iford Manor - The Peto Garden	137
Ightham Mote (The National Trust)	78
Kentchurch Court Garden	70
Kiftsgate Court Garden	55
King John's Garden & Nursery	122
Kingston Lacy (The National Trust)	45
Kingston Maurward Gardens & Animal Park	46
Laskett Gardens (The)	71
Logan Botanic Gardens	164
Loseley Park	116
Lost Gardens of Heligan (The)	28
Lullingstone Castle & World Garden	79
Lydney Park Spring Gardens	56
Marks Hall Gardens & Arboretum	48
Marle Place	80
Marwood Hill Gardens	40
Matara Gardens	57
Melbourne Hall & Gardens	34
Merriments Gardens	123
Mill Dene Garden	58
Misarden Park	59
Moors Meadow Garden & Nursery	72
Mount Pleasant Garden	21
Myddelton House Gardens	87
National Botanic Garden of Wales	174
National Garden Scheme	4
Ness Botanic Gardens	22
Newby Hall & Gardens	147
Normanby Hall Country Park	84
Nymans	129
Paignton Zoological & Botanical Gardens	41
Painshill Landscape Garden	117
Painswick Rococo Garden	60
Parham House & Gardens	130
Pashley Manor Gardens	124
Peckover House & Garden	17
Pencarrow	29
Penshurst Place & Gardens	81
Pensthorpe	92
Peter Beales Rose Gardens	93
Picton Castle Gardens & Gallery	175
Plas Tan Y Bwlch	176
Ragley Hall	132
Ramster Gardens	118
Renishaw Hall Gardens	35
Ridley's Cheer Garden	138
Ripley Castle Gardens	148
Rode Hall Gardens	23
Rodmarton Manor	61
Rousham	103
Royal Botanic Garden Edinburgh	165
Ryton Gardens	133
Samares Manor Gardens	154
Sandringham	94
Savill Garden - Windsor Great Park	8
Secret of Gardens of Sandwich (The)	82
Sheffield Park Garden - The National Trust	125
Sir Harold Hillier Gardens	66
Spetchley Park Gardens	141
St Mary's House & Gardens	131
Stillingfleet Lodge Garden and Nursery	149
Stonor Park & Gardens	104
Stonyford Cottage Gardens	24
Stourhead	139
Sudeley Castle Gardens & Exhibitions	62
Sutton Park	150
Swiss Garden (The)	7
Syon House Gardens & Park	88
Thorp Perrow	151
Titsey Place Gardens	119
Trewidden	30
Trewithen Gardens	31
Valley Gardens - Windsor Great Park	9
Waddesdon Manor	12
Waterperry Gardens	105
Wentworth Castle Gardens	152
West Green House Gardens	67
Westonbirt The National Arboretum	63
Winderwath	33
Wollerton Old Hall Garden	107
Yorkshire Lavender	153